Community Development in Primary Care –
a guide to involving the community in COPC

Also in this series:

Community-Oriented Primary Care: A Resource for Developers

COPC Depression and Anxiety Intervention Guide

COPC – A Public Health Experiment in Primary Care

Community Development in Primary Care – a guide to involving the community in COPC

Richard Freeman, Stephen Gillam,
Chris Shearin & Julian Pratt

 Fund

Published by
King's Fund Publishing
11–13 Cavendish Square
London W1M 0AN

© King's Fund 1997

First published 1997

ISBN 1 85717 123 3

A CIP catalogue record for this book is available from the British Library

Distributed by Grantham Book Services Limited
Isaac Newton Way
Alma Park Industrial Estate
GRANTHAM
Lincolnshire
NG31 9SD
Tel: 01476 541 080
Fax: 01476 541 061

Cover illustration by Clare Youngs

Contents

Preface

The purpose of this publication is to support primary care and community-based teams wishing to involve their community in service planning and delivery. It is designed to make material about effective interventions accessible to every member of the team. Much of the material presented is already available from many sources. What is distinctive about this guide is that it reworks this material within the community-oriented primary care (COPC) framework. COPC has an action orientation, and the material is presented to support team members to identify and implement appropriate change.

The King's Fund Primary Care Group has produced a series of publications to support its COPC programme. The COPC approach was introduced in a step-by-step guide entitled *Community-Oriented Primary Care – A resource for developers*, published in 1994. This publication is one of a series designed to help local teams as they work through the COPC framework. It introduces the ideas upon which community development is based and some case studies of how community development interventions have been used in primary care settings. It is designed to help primary and community-focused teams work through a process of deciding whether they wish to adopt a community development approach and to select appropriate methods.

In the initial evaluation of the COPC programme it was reported that the approach adopted by many practices could best be described as population-oriented primary care and that only a minority really involved their communities in choosing or implementing change. It was felt that many teams needed more help to understand how community involvement can be organised.

To meet this need the King's Fund team convened an expert multi-disciplinary steering group. With their help we have drawn together material to help team members answer the questions: What is community development? How can it be useful? How do we implement this approach? The guide also reports some experiences of using community development methods in general and community-based practice.

We would like to acknowledge the members of the steering group who have directed us towards the literature and have helped to shape this guide from concept to reality:

Richard Freeman, Stephen Gillam, Scott Murray, Hilary Neve, Sue Porter, Jill Russell, Chris Shearin, Gareth Williams, Amanda Gosling, Lorna Hill, Chris Jones, Mandy Wearne, Barbara Wheeler-Early

We would also like to thank all those who helped by reading and commenting on the earlier drafts of the document:

Lorna Hill, Victoria Ononeze, Helen Howson, Jill Russell, Jill Vincent, Stephen Gillam.

Last but not least, we would like to thank Richard Freeman for the care and skill with which he has crafted this very readable document from so many diverse sources.

King's Fund Primary Care Group
February 1997

Chapter 1

Introduction

This guide has been written for all those who are interested in developing community development health programmes, for example:

- primary health care teams (PHCTs);
- community development workers and agencies;
- workers in voluntary bodies;
- workers in local authorities.

It may also prove useful to others, such as staff in health commissions.

The guide can be read by individuals or teams but it assumes that individual readers will be working with others in their teams and with other agencies when implementing community development.

1.1 Primary care and community development

Community development offers primary care the benefits of individuals and community groups actively participating in their health care. This helps in:

- using resources more effectively since it helps release (and even expand) the resources of the community;
- identifying health goals and health programmes which are more relevant to local needs;
- identifying those who most need health care and, at the same time, helps develop ways of making that care accessible to them;
- supporting people's desire to take more responsibility for their own well-being.[1]

1.2 Issues

The issues that the guide addresses are:

---

1. World Health Organization 1991, p 5.

- what is community development in health and how does it differ from other forms of patient involvement?
- how has community development been used in health and what benefits are claimed for this approach?
- what are the methods available to implement community development programmes in health?
- what are the agencies with whom PHCTs can work to develop programmes?
- how can programmes be developed and run?
- what skills are needed and how can they be acquired?
- how can programmes be evaluated?

We also assume that the team has been trained in community-oriented primary care (COPC) methodology and has access to a copy of *Community-Oriented Primary Care: A resource for developers.*[2]

1.3 Objectives and overall purpose

As a result of using this guide, you should be able to:

- select the meaning of 'community development in health' that matches your team's interests and your community's needs from the range of meanings in current use;
- take account of the benefits and limitations of using community development in health when designing a programme;
- be able to plan a community development initiative with other local agencies and the community;
- select those methods used in community development that are most suitable for your situation or programme;
- identify the skills needed for your programme and arrange skills development as needed;
- plan an appropriate evaluation of the programme.

1.4 What is COPC?

The origin of this guide lies in the King's Fund work on community-oriented primary care.[3]

---

2. King's Fund 1994
3. King's Fund 1994.

COPC is an approach which seeks to promote better health through the strategic use of primary care resources. Through the early identification of health problems, it seeks to offer interventions that will promote health and prevent further illness. COPC is one way of trying to use fixed resources to greater effect.

COPC has been defined as 'a continuous process by which primary health care is provided to a defined community on the basis of its assessed health needs by the planned integration of public health with PC practice'.[4] While the focus of primary health care is usually the individual patient, with COPC the focus is the community and the individual. Thus, a programme will be aimed not only at those patients who are under treatment, but also at (a) those who have not been diagnosed, and (b) those at high risk. The community development aspect of COPC assumes that part of the implementation will be changes to the community and its environment. In this respect, COPC might be seen as a top-down approach. On the other hand, community development seeks to make changes *with* the community and is a bottom-up approach. To be effective, these two approaches need to be brought together: this guide discusses how that can be done.

The COPC cycle

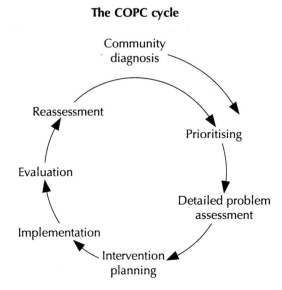

Figure 1 The COPC cycle[5]

4. King's Fund 1994.
5. King's Fund 1994.

The stages in a COPC programme are illustrated in Figure 1. In some COPC initiatives, each stage in the cycle would be seen as a task for the PHCT. In a community development approach, each stage would be seen as a shared task for the community and the PHCT.

1.5 Choosing your intervention

This guide is about community development in health and is not a guide to the effectiveness of particular interventions. It therefore needs to be used alongside appropriate sources of information on effectiveness, such the work of the NHS Centre for Reviews and Dissemination.[6]

---

6. NHS Centre for Reviews and Dissemination 1995.

Chapter 2

What is community development?

2.1 Aims and philosophy

Community development has been defined in many different ways. Typical definitions include:

- Community development is a way of tackling a community's problems by using the energy and leadership of the people who live there.[7]
- Community development is a process by which people are involved in collectively defining and taking action on the issues that affect their lives. The process is collective, but the experience is individual. Community development seeks to enable individuals and communities to grow and change according to their own needs and priorities.[8]
- CIH [community involvement in health] is essentially a process whereby people, both individually and in groups, exercise their right to play an active and direct role in the development of appropriate health services, in ensuring the conditions for sustained better health, and in supporting the empowerment of communities for health development.[9]
- Community development encompasses a commitment to a holistic approach to health which recognises the central importance of social support and social networks. A community development way of working attempts to facilitate individual and collective action around common needs and concerns. These concerns and needs are identified by people themselves, rather than being imposed from outside.[10]

Approaches to health promotion

The community development approach to health promotion can be thought of as one of four options depending on whether the approach is authoritative or negotiated and whether it is focused on the individual

7. Thomas DN 1995.
8. Labyrinth Training – unpublished materials.
9. World Health Organization 1991, p 9.
10. Adams L 1989, p 180.

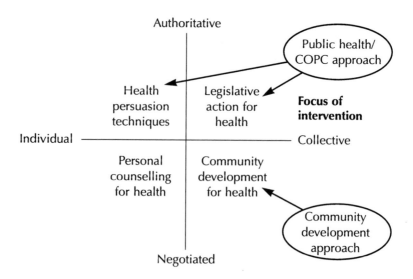

Mode of intervention

Figure 2 Strategies for health promotion[11]

or the community. The four approaches that arise from combining these variables are illustrated in Figure 2. In this guide the community development approach (bottom right in the figure) has been adopted as the model which emphasises a population approach. The other three approaches are aimed at the individual (the left-hand side of the figure) rather than the effects on health of things the individual cannot change (e.g. poverty, pollution). Those that are authoritative (the ones in the top half of the figure) ignore the fact that changes are more likely to work if people have chosen them for themselves.

ISSUES   ISSUES   ISSUES   ISSUES   ISSUES   ISSUES   ISSUES   ISSUES   ISSUES

Consider some of your team's current health promotion activities. Where do they lie in Figure 2?

Where do you wish to see future programmes lying?

Rationales for participation

The word 'participation' is used to mean many things, from persuading people that they do not want any service changes to enabling groups to run services for themselves. Arnstein has suggested eight levels of

---

11. Beattie A 1991, p 167 (Adapted).

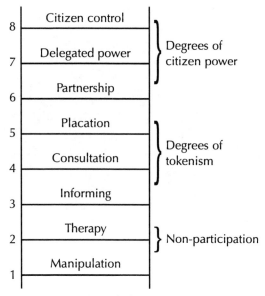

Figure 3 The ladder of citizen participation[12]

participation in what she calls the ladder of citizen participation. These are illustrated in Figure 3.

Participation can be justified at various levels, being seen as:

* a means of improving individual lifestyles, e.g. by encouraging 'healthy choices';
* a process that in itself brings benefits to the individual, since increased participation leads to increased control over one's life;
* a process which benefits the health service, since user participation can produce more appropriate use of resources;
* helping to reduce resource use. For example, through diabetic patients taking more exercise;
* a means of creating a healthier environment, both physical and social, in which people have the power to ensure that resources are used to best promote health.[13]

It is in this last, all-embracing sense that this guide uses the term participation. This implies participation at all levels of the WHO pyramid (see Figure 4).[14]

12. Arnstein 1969, p 217.
13. Murray SA (nd).
14. World Health Organization 1981.

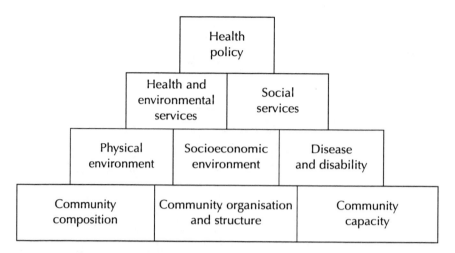

Figure 4 The WHO pyramid

ISSUES ISSUES ISSUES ISSUES ISSUES ISSUES ISSUES ISSUES ISSUES

Think of some health promotion programmes that you have been involved in. Where would they lie on the ladder of participation?

Where do you wish your future programmes to lie?

What is the rationale that your current work attaches to participation?

Communities and health

People's health is affected by their quality of life, the quality of the environment within which they live and their degree of empowerment. The following are examples of the impacts of the community on health:

- poor housing can affect health, e.g. damp and cold can produce respiratory problems and hypothermia; overcrowding and noise can produce stress;
- job insecurity, redundancy and unemployment have been linked to physical and mental illness;
- traffic, a lack of footpaths and cycle paths, dumped cars and other waste (especially in play areas) can contribute to accidents;
- a lack of supportive relationships and community networks can affect mental and physical health;
- more generally, people's health is affected by the extent to which they feel they have self-determination and are in control of their lives.[15]

15. Thomas DN 1995, p 10.

Taking this last point as the core issue, community development can be seen as 'the means for residents to exercise greater control and personal effectiveness by involving them in activities to improve the community in which they live'.[16]

The medical versus the community view

Workers in a community health project in Scotland noted a contrast between the purpose of the project as seen by local doctors and the purpose as seen by local people.

> '... the interpretation made by medical personnel was that the project would convince local people to take more preventive action within a medical model, for example, go for cervical screening, stop smoking, take up immunisation. However, the topics raised by local people as crucial to their health tended to relate to the socio-economic and emotional distress in the community.'

> '... groups of health professionals tended to view the issue of housing as a "political" one, which would take them outside their brief which they defined as health care of the individual.'[17]

A community view

> 'One of the recurring surprises of working with a health project is the solutions provided by its different perspective. For example, our practice area is very hilly and our response to the bronchitic and angina-ridden patients was to increase their medication. The project's response was to negotiate with the local council to provide a bus route through the estate to Sainsbury's!'[18]

ISSUES ISSUES ISSUES ISSUES ISSUES ISSUES ISSUES ISSUES ISSUES

For your team, what will be the key contrasts between a community development approach and what exists now?

---

16. Thomas DN 1995, p 10.
17. Hunt S 1990, pp 181–182.
18. Fisher 1994, quoted in Russell 1995.

Principles

From the definitions discussed above, some key principles of community development in health can be identified. It:

- (usually) seeks out those who feel they have little power over their own lives;
- promotes the idea of people acting together to create change;
- assumes that many of the factors that affect the health of individuals cannot be changed by the individual;
- is democratic and built on the notion of empowerment;
- promotes the sharing of knowledge and skills both between individuals and between organisations;
- values the process itself as a means of developing self-confidence and self-esteem;
- involves the community in the definition of the issues.

The concept of community involvement starts with the existing structures, which it may seek to change or enhance. One strategy (Figure 5) emphasises the interconnectedness of the structures. Community development is not any one part of the figure, but is the effect of all the elements in the figure working together. At the top of the figure, individuals and groups in the community are helped to develop. On the right-hand side, the networks between groups and organisations in the community are strengthened. On the left-hand side, links are encouraged between professionals so they are aware of what their colleagues are doing and can support each other. At the bottom of the figure, the organisations involved are encouraged to change and develop in ways which strengthen their capacity to work with communities. Finally, in the centre of the figure, the word 'overview' emphasises the need to keep the other four elements working together.

Figure 5 The elements of a community involvement strategy[19]

19. Health Promotion Wales 1996, p 4.

ISSUES ISSUES ISSUES ISSUES ISSUES ISSUES ISSUES ISSUES ISSUES

The model in Figure 5 raises the question 'Who takes the strategic overview?'

A PHCT's answer to this question can help define how that team sees the role of community development in its work.

The activities of community development

The process of community development is characterised by certain ways of working with the community, including:

- *profiling and analysis*: developing, with the community, a profile of the community's needs and resources;
- *capacity building*: using participative techniques and training to draw out the skills of the community;
- *organising*: building sustainable and accessible organisations around community issues;
- *networking*: building links between organisations;
- resourcing: helping groups gain access to funds and other resources, e.g. professional skills;
- *negotiating*: helping the community to negotiate with providers.[20]

Contrast with conventional health care

The WHO has contrasted community involvement in health with conventional health care. The latter emphasises the role of professionals doing things to individuals. The community involvement in health (CIH) approach emphasises people working with professionals to solve their problems in ways that suit them. This contrast is summarised in Table 1.

2.2 Who or what is the community?

So far, this guide has used the term community without any discussion of what that term might mean. This section will look at how the term is used and at who the community might be for any given initiative.

---

20. Taylor M 1992, pp 7–9.
21. World Health Organization 1991

Table 1 Comparison of conventional health care and CIH[21]

Conventional health care	Community involvement in health (CIH)
Use of individual leaders	Development of group links
Education as the delivery of knowledge	Education as a joint exploration of knowledge
Verbal and written communication of knowledge	Use of participatory educational methods such as games and drama in communication on health issues
Central role of (community) health worker operating through individual contacts	(Community) health workers as a group resource
Individual home visits	Workshops and seminars on health problems and issues
Individual consultation	Open-door consultation as a mechanism for involvement

The term 'community' is used in many different senses. Descriptions and definitions may concentrate on the characteristics of its members (e.g. age, ethnicity, occupation or place) or on the common interests of its members (e.g. cultural heritage, social relationships, common economic interests).[22]

A typical definitions from those working in community development in health is:

A community is a group of people who share an interest or a common set of circumstances.[23]

22. Taylor M 1992, pp 3–4.
23. Labyrinth Training – unpublished materials.

ISSUES ISSUES ISSUES ISSUES ISSUES ISSUES ISSUES ISSUES ISSUES

Which of the following factors does your team use to describe the community?

Age   ❑

Sex   ❑

Ethnicity   ❑

Occupation   ❑

Place   ❑

Culture   ❑

Social relationships   ❑

Economic interests   ❑

Other   ❑

Community, participation and consultation

The term 'participation' is also used alongside 'community' where community development is seen as one way to promote participation. However, 'participation' is sometimes confused with consumerism, which is about individual choice, whereas participation and community development are about collective action for change. Also, participation implies a redistribution of power.[24]

The term 'consultation' is another word which is sometimes used interchangeably with 'participation' but, again, consultation does not imply any shift of power. A practice or a consortium which consults need make no commitment to share decision making as a result of that consultation. On the other hand, participation or community development which did not involve shared decision making would be a contradiction in terms.

Community groups

Community groups are central to community development, since they are both a resource and a route through to individuals. Knowing which groups are active in a community and what they do is crucial to planning any community development project.

---

24. Murray SA (nd).

Community groups can be thought of as being of various types (e.g. neighbourhood groups), with a focus (single issue or general), a spread (a single community or wider) and a purpose (e.g. self-help). A system for categorising groups on this basis is shown in Figure 6.

Type
Neighbourhood: e.g. tenants' association
Interest: e.g. pensioners' group
Users: e.g. of maternity services

Focus
Single issue: e.g. health group, children's play
General focus: e.g. community association

Spread
Single community: e.g. young women's group
Federation/coalition: e.g. city federation of neighbourhood community associations

Purpose
Self-help: e.g. support group
Service delivery: e.g. holiday play scheme
Campaign: e.g. to press for policy changes

Figure 6 A method of categorising community groups[25]

ISSUES ISSUES ISSUES ISSUES ISSUES ISSUES ISSUES ISSUES ISSUES

Which are the main groups known to your team at present?

For each one:

- what is its type? (neighbourhood; interest; users);

- what is its focus? (single issue; general focus);

- spread? (single community; federation/coalition);

- purpose? (self-help; service delivery; campaign).

In each case, what does this suggest about the relevance of the group to your project?

---

25. Labyrinth Training – unpublished materials.

Representativeness

All the methods in this guide rely on participation to meet needs identified by the community. This raises the question of who speaks for the community. Those who speak for the community may be:

- *formal representatives*: e.g. community workers, project leaders and local councillors. Will they always know what the people they represent think and feel? Will the people wish to be represented rather than directly involved?
- *active citizens*: often such people are the better off and the better educated. Is what they say representative of all the community?

However, people who are poor or disadvantaged (i.e. those most likely to benefit from a community development approach) may not be represented by either of these two sources.[26] (The need to ensure that those who are consulted genuinely represent all the community is an issue that arises again under evaluation (Chapter 7).)

ISSUES ISSUES ISSUES ISSUES ISSUES ISSUES ISSUES ISSUES ISSUES

Make a list of those people and groups with whom your team has most contact for the purposes of participation.

Then make notes against each one on:

■   in what ways the contact is representative;

■   in what ways the contact might not be representative.

What are the implications of this for your participatory and community work (e.g. through funding meetings)?

Are there ways in which you can enable your contacts to be more representative?

---

26. Adams L 1989, p 181.

○ ○

Patient awareness and participation

A practice with a long-established patient participation group (around 18 years) studied awareness of it and who attended. Only 45 per cent of patients knew of its existence and only 7 per cent had ever attended a meeting.

Awareness and attendance were lower in: men; patients between 16 and 29 years; those in social classes 4 and 5; single people; and those who smoked.

More significantly from the point of view of representativeness, 'A large proportion of attenders were members of other local organisations. Awareness and interest in the group tended to be greatest in older women and those patients in social classes 1 and 2.'

The authors commented, 'This anomaly may, at its worst, encourage the development of inappropriate health care strategies and perpetuate inequalities of health within the practice population.'[27]

Building on existing structures

Many of the existing resources and networks in a community can be used to develop greater involvement in promoting health. For example, existing user groups, consumer groups, self-help groups and voluntary organisations can all provide the basis for developing involvement. The interest of individuals can also be harnessed with the hope that they might be drawn into one or more groups. Where no groups exist, locality groups might be encouraged by the statutory or community groups. Once such a structure has been identified, various methods of working with it can be employed. Some of these are summarised in Table 2.

2.3 The uses of community development in health

Community development can be used for a variety of purposes. Within the health sector, it can be used to help local people to:

- obtain better access to information about health and other community issues;
- identify and articulate their own health needs and agenda with a view to action;

27. Agass M et al. 1991.
28. Taylor P 1995, p 18 (adapted).

Table 2 Structures and methods of working [28]

Structure in the community	Methods of working with it
Individuals	• Complaint and feedback procedures • Regular opportunities for consultation • Surveys • Focus groups • Individual service plans • Consumer panels/Citizens' juries
User/consumer groups; self-help groups	• Residents' groups • Quality action circles • User panels and user forums • User advisory groups networks
Voluntary sector	• Develop a database • Shared information exchange • Regular liaison and discussion • Joint events • Collaboration in/provision of service development
Locality groups	• Community profiles • Health awareness days • Local consultations with existing groups • Networking • Information exchange • Joint projects

- start and manage their own neighbourhood organisations and groups;
- set up and run community facilities, events and activities;
- campaign or negotiate for health-giving improvements in an area, such as better play or leisure facilities, improved transport links, more work opportunities, as well as improvements to sub-standard housing;
- strengthen community networks, relationships and supports, providing mutual aid for better health;
- promote a stronger sense of community spirit and solidarity, helping to foster people's sense of worth, identity and belonging, providing an antidote to isolation and feelings of helplessness;
- develop self-esteem, confidence and personal skills.[29]

29. Thomas DN 1995.

ISSUES   ISSUES   ISSUES   ISSUES   ISSUES   ISSUES   ISSUES   ISSUES   ISSUES

What might be the key purposes of your community development programme?

○ ○

Healthy Sheffield

The approach taken by the city of Sheffield is based on a holistic concept of health, a social model of health and seven key principles.

A holistic concept of health

Health is seen as a state of complete physical, mental and social well-being and not just the absence of disease ... perceptions of health are diverse and vary according to people's cultural and social backgrounds; consequently, it is important to acknowledge people's own views about their health, not only 'expert' or professional views.

A social model of health

People's opportunities for health are influenced and constrained by inter-relating social, economic and environmental factors such as poverty, racism, unemployment, housing, child care ... Healthy Sheffield is concerned that all local policies, services and activities, for example, housing, transport, environment, are health sensitive and health promoting.

Principles

❑   Right to health

❑   Equity in health

❑   Empowerment

❑   Community participation

❑   Accountability

❑   Partnership

❑   National and international co-operation and advocacy.[30]

---

30. Healthy Sheffield Support Team 1993, pp 10–11.

○ ○

A parent support group in Calgary

This nurse-supported group built the main community development principles into its statement of principles:

❏ the group is for families and parents are in control;
❏ the group believes in and uses democratic principles to arrive at consensus;
❏ any family can join;
❏ a creative and supportive atmosphere will be encouraged within the group.[31]

Access to information

When defining needs, PHCTs may find that some of the data which they is possessed by the community. Figure 7 suggests that practices need a combination of practice data, locally published data and local data. The practice and published data are those broadly in the top part of the figure. The unpublished data are those broadly in the bottom part of the figure. Community involvement can give access to the unpublished data.

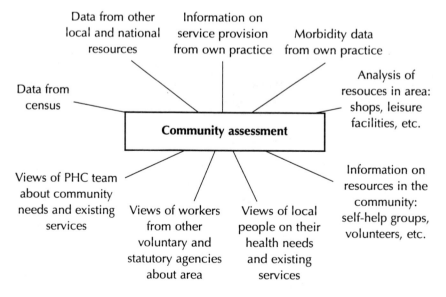

Figure 7 Community assessment and its data sources[32]

31. Rutherford G and Campbell D 1993, p 27.
32. Neve H (nd).

ISSUES ISSUES ISSUES ISSUES ISSUES ISSUES ISSUES ISSUES ISSUES

What data does your practice use to learn about the community?

(You might wish to link these data with the issues on representativeness discussed earlier.)

Community development and *Health for All* targets

Current progress towards the *Health for All* targets will not lead to their being met by the target dates. One analysis of the slow progress towards these targets shows that it is essential to be more responsive to need and to look beyond strictly medical solutions:

> '*Indeed it is argued that the target of Health for All will be unattainable unless radically different forms of health care are put into practice, permitting the development of health services that are people's services, responsive not only to people's needs in respect of health and development, and encompassing more than just services designed and maintained by health personnel or focused solely on medical care.*'[33]

The changes in emphasis suggested by the WHO are the same ones that a community development approach would employ.

Practical manifestations of involvement

Involvement is about people taking an active role in improving health. This can take many forms, including:

- volunteering/activism;
- fund-raising;
- complaining;
- information giving and receiving;
- consulting on specific agendas;
- involvement in planning and decision-making processes;
- joint working and collaboration in developing new services;
- joint working on values and principles for purchasing in primary care;
- a growing partnership approach between primary care and the public.[34]

---

33. World Health Organization 1991, pp 3–4.
34. Consumer Involvement Project 1994, p 7 (Adapted).

Levels of involvement in the profile process

The ladder of participation emphasises that a community's level of involvement can be anything from nil, through token to full participation. When running a project, it can be useful to both decide on the desired level of participation and to agree indicators for measuring that level. One set of measures of involvement is shown in Figure 8. The suggested factors could be varied for any one project, and what would constitute 'low' or 'high' would also need to be agreed.

Community involvement in:

High   **Low**

Initiating profile

Determining the issues to be reviewed

Determining methodology

Through being interviewed

Data collection

Data analysis

Presenting the findings

Action on the findings

Evaluation of the process

Figure 8 Scales for measuring levels of involvement[35]

ISSUES ISSUES ISSUES ISSUES ISSUES ISSUES ISSUES ISSUES ISSUES

The factors chosen for the scales in Figure 8 are unlikely to apply to all projects. For your team, what are the particular areas in which you wish to encourage participation?

You may wish to return to this issue once you have looked at the section on evaluation.

35. Labyrinth Training (adapted) – unpublished materials.

Empowerment

Taylor describes empowerment as 'the right of everyone, regardless of their circumstances, to have more control over their lives and to influence the decisions which affect them' and goes on to identify four ways in which empowerment can be achieved in health and social services:

- by providing accessible *information* so that people know enough about the service to make decisions; 'accessible' here means things such as non-technical and in the user's own first language;
- through *access and equity*, e.g. wheelchair access to buildings, appointments at times that fit people's other commitments;
- through *choice* being possible;
- through *redress and representation*, e.g. a well-publicised complaints procedure.[36]

Empowerment, though, is not just about enabling a group of people to take more control of their own lives. One group can only gain power at the expense of another group relinquishing it.

> ISSUES ISSUES ISSUES ISSUES ISSUES ISSUES ISSUES ISSUES ISSUES
>
> In what ways will your project promote empowerment within the four categories of: *information, access and equity, choice* and *redress and representation?*

2.4 Rural community development

Community development health projects seem largely to have been in urban areas. However, the need for such developments in rural areas is just as great. For example:

- the rural population tends to be older: 8.1 per cent are over 75 in rural England compared to 7 per cent for England as a whole;
- the rural population tends to include more people on low incomes: 18 per cent of men (compared to 8 per cent nationally) and 54 per cent of women (47 per cent nationally) are on low wages;
- the rural population tends to have less access to health care services: 74 per cent of parishes have no general practice; and 32 per cent of rural households have no car (23 per cent nationally).[37]

---

36. Taylor P 1995, p 9.
37. ACRE 1994.

Where appraisals have been carried out, they seem to have lead to action, including the use of village halls for surgeries and improved public transport. The key agencies seem to be the parish council and the local Women's Institute. Beyond the village, the Rural Community Council is often the most active body.[38]

Some work has been done on collating information about health care problems in rural areas (see the list below) but the list seems to refer to 1985 (although it appears in a 1992 publication) and there is no indication as to whether there was any community involvement in identifying these needs.

An example of a rural project (Brockenhurst Healthy Village Project) appears in Chapter 6.

○ ○

Health care issues in rural areas

❏ Poor awareness of fares to hospital scheme

❏ High cost of transport to health services

❏ Lack of transport to health services

❏ Difficulties over running surgeries from village halls

❏ Lack of parish council involvement in health issues

❏ Lack of knowledge on health service structure/planning processes

❏ Lack of knowledge/information sharing by campaign groups (e.g. fighting a hospital closure)

❏ Difficulties of establishing self-help initiatives in rural areas

❏ Lack of sensitivity/understanding of rural needs by chcs

❏ Health authority policies insensitive to rural needs

❏ Need to encourage more resources to community/parish-based care

❏ Cuts in ambulance and hospital car service

❏ Lack of official recognition of wider social care role of rural GPs

❏ Poor provision of ante-natal and maternity services in rural areas.[39]

---

38. Fennell 1992.
39. Fennell 1992, pp 15–16.

2.5 Stages in community development

Community development is a long-term process that requires a systematic approach with careful planning, implementation and evaluation. Individual projects take time (see below) and the process of community development is itself developmental. It has been suggested that this process goes through four stages:

- *isolation/ignorance*: when the community has no access to involvement and is unaware of how it could become involved;
- *utilisation*: where the community receives health benefits but is not actively involved in planning or implementation;
- *resource contribution*: where the community starts to contribute resources and becomes involved in some aspects of the programme;
- *community control*: where the community is responsible for setting health priorities and for planning, implementation, monitoring and evaluation of health programmes with the professional agencies in a supporting role.[40]

This progression emphasises that community development projects will have varying degrees of involvement according to what various parties feel comfortable with.

ISSUES ISSUES ISSUES ISSUES ISSUES ISSUES ISSUES ISSUES ISSUES

Think of some health initiatives that you have been involved in.

Where on the four point scale (*isolation/ignorance; utilisation; resource contribution; community control*) do they come?

Individual projects

Projects may go through many stages, including some of the following:

1 Entry: getting to know the community or the organisation in which you are working;
2 Building up contacts and trust; clarifying roles;
3 Identifying formal and informal networks and structures;
4 Working with others to identify the main concerns, problems and areas of common interest;

---

40. World Health Organization 1991, p 13 (adapted).

5 Identifying what needs to change;

6 Establishing a sense of involvement, participation and commitment;

7 Identifying opportunities and problems;

8 Developing strategies and tactics to bring about change by building on the openings and questioning or avoiding the resistances;

9 Taking action;

10 Evaluating;

11 Continuing the process.[41]

2.6 Benefits/limitations of community development

Developing community methods involves enormous commitment; many difficulties may have to be overcome. One study of the use of community methods in general practice found a wide range of benefits and issues identified by primary care staff. The benefits included:

- more satisfying work;
- more appropriate patient use of the services and hence more effective use;
- more realistic patient expectations;
- GPs felt that they had a greater knowledge of the resources to offer patients;
- reduced drug prescribing and more recommendation of complementary therapies (e.g. relaxation classes and yoga);
- a feeling of being able to share problems with other agencies.

However, in the same study, the above list was balanced by a range of problems, including:

- lack of time;
- lack of financial incentive;
- lack of appropriate skills (e.g. in research methods and community methods);
- distrust of qualitative methods;
- practices rarely correspond with natural communities;
- a challenge to the professional control of health;
- concern that asking will lead to overwhelming demands;
- lack of support from other team members;
- too much change.[42]

41. Labyrinth Training (adapted) – unpublished materials.
42. Neve H (nd).

ISSUES ISSUES ISSUES ISSUES ISSUES ISSUES ISSUES ISSUES ISSUES

If you have had experience of projects involving community agencies or some other method of participation, make a list of the benefits and problems that you experienced.

How did you overcome the problems?

What did you learn?

Supporting other initiatives

Given that community development is a method which includes participation and consultation, it can be an effective means of supporting other health programmes such as Local Voices, the Patient's Charter and locality purchasing. It can also support GPs in advocating patient and public needs.

For example, there are clear links between the ideas of locality purchasing and those of community development in health. A review of locality plans in four counties found that their emphasis was on:

- information gathering and communicating;
- identifying and assessing local health care needs (and in some cases social needs);
- building local joint working relationships with local organisations;
- listening to and talking through diverse views.[43]

These functions have much in common with community development but the potential to use community development for implementation has not always been recognised. The same study noted:

> 'Once local knowledge has been collated and profiles produced, it is not always clear how this can be effectively fed into county commissioning activities, or how it can contribute to the development of local projects to improve health without increasing management overheads.'[44]

43. Bryttan Y 1994, p 3.
44. Bryttan Y 1994, p 3

ISSUES ISSUES ISSUES ISSUES ISSUES ISSUES ISSUES ISSUES ISSUES

Make a list of the current health initiatives in which you are involved.

Against each, note any ways in which you think community development could help with the initiative.

Chapter 3

Why use community development for health?

3.1 The policy and organisational background

Access and inequalities

The Black Report noted that 'inequalities in health [are] perpetuated from the cradle to the grave' and that '... the availability of good medical care tends to vary inversely with the need of the population served.'[45] The need to address health inequalities has also been highlighted by the Department of Health.[46] Community development can be seen as a response to these inequalities, seeking to mobilise local resources to change the relevance, quality and quantity of health care in a community.[47]

Poverty

A particular manifestation of inequality is the link between poverty and ill health. As the study *Poverty and Health* says:

> 'Poverty makes people sick. While death comes sooner for people in poverty, life is also plagued with ill health. Children in social classes IV and V suffer more chest and ear infections. Long-term illness is more than twice as likely for unskilled workers than for those in professional jobs. The difference is even bigger when people are asked to describe their own health – instead of having it measured for them. While 12 per cent of men in class I describe their health as only fair or poor, the figure is tripled in class V.'[48]

45. Quoted in Somerville G 1984, p 19 and p23.
46. Department of Health 1995.
47. Somerville G 1984, chapter 3.
48. Laughlin S and Black D (eds) 1995, p 28.

○ ○

Improving access to benefits

In West Bromwich, Citizens' Advice Bureau staff attend four local practices in order to offer advice on benefits.

In 15 months they saw 1200 people with nearly 2000 problems. Through their advice, patients gained £25,000 in new benefits and rescheduled £250,000 of debt.

The service has proved particularly effective in providing advice on those benefits which are health-linked, such as those for pregnancy or long-term ill health.[49]

Government policy

Government policy has increasingly emphasised the value of involving users in the health service. While some of the emphasis is on users as individuals making individual choices (e.g. the *Patient's Charter*), other policy documents specifically refer to the need to consult the community (e.g. *Working for Patients*, *Local Voices* and *Health of the Nation*).

A particular area where benefits are claimed for user involvement is medical audit. Such benefits include: doctors acting on user pressure to support change; more knowledgeable users being less likely to request ineffective treatments; and the benefits of audit addressing patient as well as doctor concerns.[50]

The World Health Organization (WHO) *Health for All* initiative has also had a strong influence on a community development approach to health promotion, stressing as it does:

- redressing inequalities through action on the underlying social and economic determinants of inequalities in health and health-related behaviour;
- community participation in policy and planning and development;
- intersectorial collaboration between the health service and other statutory and voluntary agencies.[51]

---

49. Laughlin S and Black D (eds) 1995, p 133.
50. Joule 1992, pp 10–11.
51. Russell J 1995, p 17.

ISSUES ISSUES ISSUES ISSUES ISSUES ISSUES ISSUES ISSUES ISSUES

In what ways do you hope your team's initiative will improve access and reduce inequalities in health?

3.2 Benefits of participation

The WHO has summarised the benefits of participation under five headings:

- *coverage*: participatory projects involve more people than non-participatory projects and increase the number of beneficiaries of any development;
- *efficiency*: participation promotes the better co-ordination of resources, so increasing the efficiency of their use;
- *effectiveness*: goals, objectives, plans and strategies are more relevant as a result of participation;
- *equity*: participation helps to promote the notion of providing benefits for those in greatest need;
- *self-reliance*: participation at community level increases people's control over their lives and so promotes a sense of self-reliance.[52]

Benefits of consulting

There are many benefits which can flow from consulting the community. These include:

- it can provide feedback on the quality of your provision;
- it may identify new needs;
- it can be part of a wider strategy to involve users in policy development;
- it can be used to better shape services to users' needs;
- it helps fulfil a statutory requirement.[53]

Benefits of community development in health

Many reasons are put forward for the use of community development in health. Some writers claim direct health benefits (e.g. increased take- up and effectiveness of the service); others claim wider benefits (e.g. the general value to individuals and communities of the skills learnt through

---

52. World Health Organization 1991, p 5.
53. Wiltshire Voluntary Development Forum (nd) (p 2, adapted).

community development). Labyrinth Training and Consultancy have summarised the range of benefits of community development in health as follows:

- participation and involvement are fundamental human rights;
- interest in and validation of people's experience and views can be health-enhancing in their own right;
- community development assists the targeting of disadvantaged or isolated groups, allowing for a shift in focus from traditional priorities;
- it widens perspectives from beyond the more established voluntary organisations to smaller community groups and individuals;
- it increases take-up and effectiveness of services, as planning can be tailored more towards identified needs (both in terms of content and delivery);
- skills learnt through participation and involvement can be extended to other aspects of participant lives, e.g. employment, education and politics;
- skills learnt through facilitating and encouraging community involvement also extend and widen the expertise and perspectives of professionals;
- widening the input into policy and planning of health services opens up new opportunities for innovative and creative thinking and developments;
- community development allows for the collectivising of people's views and needs and so allows a range of individual concerns to be acted on strategically;
- it enables the formation of groups, organisations and support structures within communities which provide a resource for many members of local communities, and can play an important preventative role;
- it encourages decisions to be made by people on their own behalf, which are often more realistic and sustainable than those made for them by others;
- it encourages commitment and motivation and enhances shared responsibility and partnership approaches to local provision.[54]

54. Labyrinth Training – unpublished materials.

ISSUES ISSUES ISSUES ISSUES ISSUES ISSUES ISSUES ISSUES ISSUES

Which of the above benefits would you be seeking in a community development programme? You might find it helpful to make three lists:

■ essential benefits;

■ desirable benefits;

■ irrelevant or unimportant benefits.

○ ○

Benefits – summary of 100 projects

The *Poverty and Health* survey looked at 100 projects on poverty and health and identifyied ten areas in which benefits could be demonstrated. These are listed in Table 3.

Table 3 Achievements from a survey of 100 projects on poverty and health[55]

Type of benefit	Examples
Increasing income for individuals and communities	• employing local people • improving benefit uptake and rescheduling debt • providing support experience and references to enable people to find jobs
Improving the quality of life and well-being in communities	• making contact with people who are isolated • helping to increase self-esteem, motivation, skills, knowledge, insight and experience • local people having the opportunity to make decisions • women's enjoyment in coming to groups • effective local management committees
Providing a service	• safe and confidential counselling services for women • drop-in family centre based on users needs which is often the first port of call in a crisis • a centre of excellence for housing and benefits advice • a quality mental health service on a deprived estate

cont.

55. Laughlin S and Black D (eds) 1995, pp 102–103.

Table 3 *cont.*

Type of benefit	*Examples*
Creating a tangible outcome	• 'listen to us' health survey • accredited training on health rights and health rights volunteer scheme • new type of health centre with capital funding of £1.2 million • community garden and new playground • successful campaign for nursery school
Engaging the community and links with professionals	• local people involved in assessing needs • involvement of people in planning of mental health service • practical results of campaigning such as housing improvements and play areas
Creating or improving inter-agency work and strategy development	• forming alliances between unlikely partners • building channels of communication into decision-making processes of health authority and local authority and influencing thinking • development of inter-agency working group on poverty and health
Raising awareness of poverty and health	• increasing understanding of the social model of health • raising awareness of poverty as a rural issue • raising the profile on the link between poverty and poor health
Developing new health issues	• identifying racial harassment as a health issue • creating awareness of income and accommodation as health issues among mental health professionals
Promoting lifestyle issues	• framework for field workers working on food/diet related issues • making community development relevant to coronary heart disease
Developing a quality project and keeping going	• doubling of the workforce, including funding for an Asian woman worker • clear identify of project in locality • continuity for local users of project • being trusted by the community and providing a reliable service

○ ○

Carers' panels benefits in Birmingham

The following benefits were identified in a carers' panels project which involved a local authority carers' unit, a social services department and health agencies.

Benefits for carers

❑ Carers are high on agencies' agendas and issues feed into policy

❑ Direct access to senior managers by carers

❑ Carers able to influence services by involvement in planning process

❑ Monitoring of services

❑ Involvement of many internal groups and training in city council, health and FHSA

❑ Carers have become 'campaigners' on behalf of all carers in Birmingham

Benefits for agencies

❑ Ready-made 'consumer group' of carers to enable statutory agencies to tailor their services appropriately to meet the needs of carers and those cared for

❑ A 'collective' view from carers to assist the planning process

❑ Ensures carers activities are carer-centred

❑ Informs policy[56]

---

56. Taylor P and Upward J 1995, section 5.

○ ○

Health workers' reasons for a community-based approach

A UK study of 24 health workers and GPs found the following reasons for involvement in community-based work:

❑ to plan better;

❑ to solve a particular health problem;

❑ to achieve equity;

❑ to promote community participation;

❑ to learn more about available resources within the community;

❑ to give people a greater say in health care decisions.[57]

○ ○

Benefits of outreach and community involvement

Chorgoria Hospital in Kenya has an extensive outreach programme which promotes self-help and uses 500 volunteer health workers and 250 trained birth attendants. As a result of this programme:

❑ child immunisation neared 90 per cent;

❑ child mortality decreased;

❑ fertility rates declined and the use of family planning services rose.

Experience of this programme led Murray to ask, 'With which aspects of health care can patients, families, communities, and the wider population be involved in Britain in the 1990s?'[58]

3.3 Benefits of access to lay knowledge

There is evidence that lay, experiential knowledge can help to identify causes of ill health that would otherwise go undetected. For example, lay people have identified problems from exposure to toxic waste, and workers and trade unions have often taken a lead in identifying relationships between disease and environmental factors at work.[59]

---

57. Neve H (nd).
58. Murray SA 1996. Letter in *British Medical Journal.*
59. Popay and Williams 1996, p 761.

Access to this type of knowledge implies a use of a wider range of research methods, especially of qualitative ones. Whereas quantitative research can establish how many people smoke in a community, only qualitative methods can identify why those people continue to smoke even though they know the risks to their health. The smokers know the reasons, yet without this lay knowledge, public health interventions are unlikely to be effective.[60]

Popay and Williams conclude:

> 'If public health research is to be more relevant and sound and lead to more appropriate and effective policy and practice, the lay experts have to be involved in the process: in generating the research questions, commenting on the research design, interpreting the findings, and developing the policy implications.'[61]

3.4 Benefits of community development for needs identification

Providing an effective primary care service depends on good needs identification. This in turn depends on knowing the health problems in the locality and the resources available for responding to those problems and on mobilising those resources.

Community development is one way of approaching these three points. These can be expanded into a checklist for primary care teams as below.

○ ○

Primary care checklist

1   Do we know where the practice population thinks the community boundaries are? (i.e. the practice population's view of the community boundaries may not coincide with the practice boundaries.)
2   Do we know what the main health problems and conditions are in each part of the community and at each age and status of life?
3   Is this information widely available in the community so that everyone is able to discuss what needs to be done to improve health?
4   Is information accessible about what health services are available and how people can get access when needed?

cont.

---

60. Popay and Williams 1996, p 763.
61. Popay and Williams 1996, p 764.

○ ○

Primary care checklist *cont.*

5   Is action being taken to create a safer, healthier physical and social environment which supports healthy lifestyles?

6   Are all the areas of everyday life, public and private, involved in planning and working for improved health?

7   Is there an effective way of getting everybody to work together at the neighbourhood level?

8   Are there identified community leaders who speak out for better health and make sure that those factors that affect health are understood by all the public?

9   Does your community have a specific plan to collect and distribute the information it needs about health, develop stronger intersectorial co-operation and provide adequate resources for health? [62]

○ ○

Needs in Hartcliffe

The health needs identified in the Hartcliffe Health Project illustrate the wide range of topics which are of concern to local communities:

❏   younger people wanted more facilities, e.g. recreation, safe play areas and a community centre;

❏   nearly one-third of people saw better housing as the best means of improving their health;

❏   more health services in the area;

❏   more understanding of problems by people who provide health care;

❏   more things to do locally;

❏   low incomes;

❏   dirty and dangerous environment, e.g. dog fouling and abandoned cars. [63]

---

62. Ashton J and Luker K 1991 (adapted).
63. Roberts E 1990.

3.5 Benefits in accessing resources

From the point of view of a PHCT, inter-agency working and working with community groups offer resource benefits, such as access to:

- the community (as opposed to access to a collection of individuals);
- the knowledge and skills of the community;
- local resources – these can be focused on an issue that you have agreed to tackle.

The resources accessed in this way include:

- skilled and experienced workers;
- skilled and experienced volunteers;
- premises – especially in locations trusted by those members of the community who are reluctant to visit surgeries and other formal places;
- funds, e.g. through joint applications.

Benefits of links with voluntary services

Primary care staff seem to see voluntary organisations as valuable for their patients. In one survey, over 50 per cent of PHCT staff felt that certain patients (the bereaved, the physically disabled, and those with life-threatening diseases) would benefit from referral to an agency. But, in the same survey, only 21 per cent of PHCT staff had recommended a patient to a voluntary agency in the previous year. Community nurses made most recommendations, which may suggest that, being closer to the agencies gave them a better understanding of how they could benefit patients. Of all the agencies recommended, the frequency varied from 63 per cent (Cruise – bereavement care) to 1 per cent (manic depressive group).

This study showed that PHCT knowledge of voluntary organisations was far from systematic and that the agencies themselves rarely took any steps to keep PHCT staff informed of what they did. The study concluded that the agencies should set up a local forum for co-ordinating information links with general practice.[64]

---

64. Bake D and Burgess R 1993.

○ ○

A general practice–voluntary sector link

A group practice in Shipston-on Stour, uncertain about the services available for people with mental health problems, invited a number of workers to a workshop co-ordinated by the community psychiatric nurse. Those attending included:

❏ members of the voluntary sector (Cruise and Relate);

❏ a local psychiatrist, a psychologist and a social worker;

❏ the day unit sister and ward sister from the local community hospital;

❏ two GPs, two practice nurses and two district nurses from the practice.

Each visitor gave a five-minute presentation about the work of their group or agency. In small groups participants then discussed the management of five different patients, and results were fed back to the entire group.
The workshop was very successful. The participants realised how little they knew about other services and learnt a great deal. The PHC team is now compiling a brief set of referral guidelines which includes a summary of the work of each agency.[65]

○ ○

The Vauxhall Health Forum

In Vauxhall, an urban deprived area of Liverpool, public meetings were held to discuss local health issues. Some of the residents who attended decided to form the Vauxhall Health Forum and developed a list of health-related priorities. The FHSA, after discussions with the forum, agreed to fund two part-time GPs to spend one year exploring these priorities before setting up a practice which, it was hoped, would be sensitive and responsive to local need.In order to learn about local people's views and concerns, the GPs decided to hold discussions with existing groups in the area: pension groups, youth clubs and school parent groups. The Forum, who met regularly, acted as a steering committee for the two GPs and were involved in planning the interviews. The aim was to find out:

1 perceived problems with existing PHC services and possible solutions;
2 perceptions of local health problems and the broader issues affecting health.

cont.

65. Richard Byng quoted in Neve (nd), p 7.

○ ○

The Vauxhall Health Forum *cont.*

A number of problems were identified, including poor communication with doctors and problems with reception areas. It appeared that people knew little about existing services (such as family planning and psycho-sexual counselling) and wanted more information, particularly on how to access clinics. Stress was the most commonly cited cause of ill health, often linked to unemployment and the lack of social amenities and people requested help for this, such as counselling.

It seemed that existing services were not being properly used because of people's negative feelings about them and because, for many people, socio-economic difficulties were more of a priority than health. The interviewers discussed with the forum how to tackle these issues. They suggested that a lay health worker should be appointed to do outreach work and that local people should be involved in planning services. They felt a café would break down the clinical air of the health centre and encourage uptake of services. The GPs intend to incorporate these ideas into their practice.[66]

ISSUES   ISSUES   ISSUES   ISSUES   ISSUES   ISSUES   ISSUES   ISSUES   ISSUES

In your team:

- how do team members get briefed about local voluntary organisations?

    – how well does this work?

- is anyone in the team responsible for collating information on local agencies (e.g. from the new national health information service)?

    – how could this service be improved?

- does anyone in the team provide an information link with the agencies (e.g. through the local volunteer bureau)?

    – how could this service be improved?

---

66. Helen McKendrick quoted in Neve (nd), p 8.

Chapter 4

How to practise community development in primary care

4.1 The local agencies and their skills

The first step in community development is to learn what exists in the community. This includes identifying:

- local services (e.g. social services and education);
- community groups;
- religious groups;
- health facilities;
- housing;
- youth clubs;
- recreational facilities;
- employment and unemployment;
- where power and leadership lies in the community (i.e. who makes the decisions?).

One effective way of finding out about many of the above activities is to consult the local authority.[67]

ISSUES ISSUES ISSUES ISSUES ISSUES ISSUES ISSUES ISSUES ISSUES

Using the above list as a basis, make a first rough list of what you know about the resources in your community.

How can this list be turned into a full description of resources (e.g. who could you go to for help in this)?

Choosing an organisational structure

There are various structures around which to base a community development project. Some of these are set out in Table 4.

---

67. Harris 1994.

More generally, there are clear disadvantages to a provider- or purchaser-led attempt to promote participation. Providers may find that:

- people are reluctant to give honest feedback;
- they focus on current users and so fail to identify the needs of non-users;
- they may be partial in how they decide to act on what they hear.

On the other hand, purchasers may find that:

- they are seen as distant from people and so lack credibility;
- their responses may be too driven by resource constraints.[68]

There may be ways of overcoming these difficulties. Where there are not, community development will need a more neutral forum within which purchasers, providers and PHCTs (in both their roles) can play a full part, escaping the drawbacks above.

4.2 Stakeholders

The notion of stakeholders is useful for a community-based project. For any one project there will be a range of people and organisations who have an interest (and a capacity to influence) the outcome. For example, the stakeholders for a community development project on carers might include, but have different agendas from, the following:

- carers;
- users;
- social services;
- PHCT staff, especially community nurses;
- local hospitals – since carers help to reduce demand on these;
- local residential homes – carers also help to reduce demand here;
- local voluntary organisations;
- town/parish/district councils;
- churches;
- local schools;
- other local groups and associations (e.g. Women's Institute, parents' groups, tenants' associations).

---

68. Taylor 1995, pp 14–15.

Table 4 Possible organisational structures

Structure	Pros	Cons
PHCT-based	• have frequent contact with clients/patients • small and flexible, so can respond to individual needs • information gained helps make purchasing decisions • can make work more satisfying • can make the practice a focus for community-based health	• lack of time and resources • solutions found may affect doctors' income • team may lack the necessary skills • those who are intimidated by doctors may not express their views • surgeries are seen as illness centres rather than health centres • solutions may only be medical ones
Local authority-based	• can work with communities – not limited to practice boundaries • flexibility to employ those with the right skills • can pump prime projects	• seen as top-down • may want quick results to justify funding • may have narrow definition of health • may employ existing workers, irrespective of skills
Project-specific independent structure (e.g. Wells Park Health Project)	• greater ownership by the community • no institutional restrictions on what can be done • can work with several practices • more likely to be seen as health-, rather than illness-related • able to look at health in wider terms	• health professionals may not take project seriously • ability to achieve change may be limited if health workers not involved • may be difficult to raise funds

ISSUES ISSUES ISSUES ISSUES ISSUES ISSUES ISSUES ISSUES ISSUES

Who will be the stakeholders for your team's initiative?

What will their main expectations be?

4.3 Making a start

Where, how and on what scale to start are difficult issues. It is not feasible, for example, for a PHCT to walk out of the surgery and start a project with local people. One approach is to see the community in four levels, as in Figure 9. The most accessible people are the community leaders at level A. While they are not able to speak for the community, they are key to gaining access to the other levels and will have a detailed knowledge of the resources, groupings and activities in the community.

At level B, there are the activists in particular areas such as work with older people or housing. They are central to work in those areas and, again, have in-depth local knowledge on the issue of concern to them. They may not, though, be effective in building links with other agencies.

Those at level C are individuals who are used to participating in groups, probably including the groups represented at level B. These people already have some of the skills needed for community development and so are a prime resource to tap into.[69]

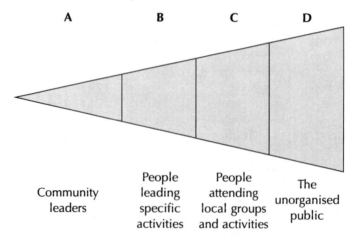

Figure 9 Levels of community activity[70]

Working from what the community says

When working through the levels in Figure 9, one needs to work *from* what the community says *to* what the community needs. This means:

- *understanding*: starting with the community's concerns;

69. Taylor P and Upward J 1995, section 4.
70. Taylor P and Upward J 1995, section 4.

- *clarifying*: working with the community to get a picture of needs;
- *action planning*: listening to what response the community wants to those needs.

The Wells Park approach (box below) is typical of how this has been done.

Starting through listening

In the Wells Park Health Project, the community health worker started with meetings with local people, asking them what they felt their health needs were. They listed:

❑ shortage of child care provision and activities for older adults;

❑ poor access for the disabled people;

❑ the cost and availability of healthy food;

❑ stress;

❑ personal safety for women;

❑ racism and prejudice;

❑ traffic problems;

❑ shortage of recreational facilities;

❑ dog mess in streets and parks.[71]

4.4 Needs assessment

'For action to be taken, health variations must be identified locally as well as nationally.'[72] Community development methods have often been seen as an effective method for such local needs identification.

Information needed

The information which is required for a needs assessment will generally come under six main headings:

---

71. Russell J 1995, p 25.
72. Department of Health 1995, p 36.

- *health and medical data*, e.g. child morbidity and mortality rates;
- *social services data*, e.g. children in care, mentally ill caseload;
- *demographic data*, e.g. unemployment, housing conditions, car ownership;
- *environmental data*, e.g. air quality, traffic, pedestrian safety, play provision;
- *poverty indicators*, e.g. gas, electricity and water disconnections;
- *residents' perceptions* of the area and its health and other needs;
- *the capacity and capabilities* of the community.[73]

Needs assessment methods

The methods of consulting fall into two main types: market research methods and democratic methods.

Market research methods include:

- quantitative surveys;
- focus groups, i.e. in-depth discussion by a group of users;
- interviews with users and others.

Democratic methods include:

- meeting people in their own groups;
- stakeholder conferences, i.e. conferences where those attending represent organisations with an interest in the issue;
- consultation workshops, i.e. meetings where a selected group of participants discuss a planned programme with a high level of participation;
- public meetings.[74]

More generally, a choice usually has to be made between *qualitative* and *quantitative* methods. Table 5 summarises the main reasons for selecting the two approaches.

---

73. Thomas DN 1995, p 13 (adapted).
74. Wiltshire Voluntary Development Forum (nd) (adapted).

Table 5 Selecting methods[75]

Quantitative surveys	Qualitative studies
Use when:	**Use when:**
• You need to make statistically-based generalisations from the findings.	• You need to explore what it means to people to behave in certain ways.
• You need measures of incidence or prevalence.	• The topics are not suitable for quantification.
• The information needs are well-enough designed to be able to create a questionnaire.	• The methods suit the target groups, e.g. they prefer discussion to the 'interrogation' of a formal survey.
• Respondents are able and willing to provide information under the constrained circumstances of a questionnaire.	• The research needs preliminary qualitative study before a full survey can be designed.

Rapid appraisal

Rapid appraisal is one qualitative method that is participative and has been proved to yield generalisable data. It is often a good tool for initial health surveys and needs assessments, particularly as it records community perceptions and engenders a degree of mutual responsibility between an agency and the community.

The method does not aim at the full participation of the community and does not have community development as its primary purpose. It does, though, yield a rapid overview of a community and its health. This is done by consulting a small number, but a wide range of participants. Typically, rapid appraisal will use three main sources:

- written records;
- interviews with a range of informants;
- observations made in the neighbourhood or in the interviewees" homes.[76]

Those consulted will typically include:

- those who work in the community on a professional basis (e.g. teachers, the police, community health workers)

75. Sykes *et al.* 1992 (Vol. 1, p 3; Vol. 2, p 5; adapted).
76. Murray *et al.* 1994, p 698.

- community leaders (e.g. councillors and church leaders)
- those who are important in informal networks (e.g. local shop owners, lollipop people).[77]

In the Dumbiedykes study the authors concluded that 'in contrast to the quantitative methods used by epidemiologists, rapid appraisal offers very specific insights, helping to define what the problems are rather than how many people are affected by them. It helps to identify the strength of feeling within the community on key issues'.[78] As a result of the study, 13 objectives for the neighbourhood were identified ranging from getting a bus into the estate to an increased role for local chemists.

○ ○

Informants in a rapid appraisal study

The following informants were consulted in the Dumbiedykes rapid appraisal study. The writers concluded 'in retrospect the first 25 interviews (10 residents and 15 local workers) would have been sufficient'.

Voluntary worker, St Ann's Community Cntre
Visiting sister, St Patrick's Roman Catholic Church
Home care organiser, social work department
Project director, South Side Care Project
Dumbiedykes Social Club convenor
Lothian regional counsellor
Project co-ordinator, Safer Edinburgh Project
District counsellor
Local community involvement police officer
Receptionist, MacKenzie Medical Centre
Community development worker
Old Town Renewal Trust
Housing department officer, Edinburgh District Council
Pharmacist
Local district nurse
Head teacher and deputy head teacher, local primary school
Volunteer, Women's Royal Voluntary Service
Community psychiatric nurse, community drugs problems service
Shopkeeper, Dumbiedykes Store
Project co-ordinator, local youth project
Local health visitor
Public transport unit, planning department, Lothian Regional Council

cont.

---

77. Ong BN and Humphris G 1994, p 66.
78. Murray *et al.* 1994, p 699–700.

○ ○

Informants in a rapid appraisal study *cont.*

Co-ordinator, Dumbiedykes Children's Centre
Recently retired local general practitionerGroup interview – South Side
Care Project board of directors
Group interview – Dumbiedykes Residents' Association
Group discussion – teenage girls at youth project
17 residents selected to represent various age groups, social situations and
health problems[79]

4.5 Consultation

Consulting in community care services

A range of methods for consulting in community care have been identified.
These include:

- consulting individuals who use or want to use the services and who
  wish to discuss their own experience;
- consulting groups of service users about their common experience;
- consulting carers about their common experience;
- consulting representatives of organisations which have relevance to
  the service, e.g. representatives of those with a caring role or
  representatives of those with physical or sensory impairment;
- consulting trainers or consultants with personal experience of the
  services and who are paid to put forward the voice of users;
- consulting charities and voluntary organisations which speak on
  behalf of users but are not controlled by them.[80]

79. Murray et al. 1994, p 699.
80. Wiltshire Voluntary Development Forum (nd) (adapted).

○ ○

Consulting parents in a general practice

One practice, concerned about the number of inappropriate visits and appointments made for young children, invited a group of parents to come together to talk about their children's health. Discussions revealed that surgery times made it difficult for some people to attend and, as a result, the practice decide to run a late surgery each day. The parents also wanted to know more about a number of health issues, including allergies, asthma, meningitis and burns. Practice staff have held follow-up sessions to discuss these. The parents now feel more confident to manage sick children, have written an article about the group in the local paper, and the possibility of these parents training others is being explored.[81]

Good practice in consulting

How consulting is approached can have a significant effect on its success. The Wiltshire Voluntary Development Forum recommend four key points to bear in mind when consulting:

- most people want to give their views on issues which they know about through personal experience;
- people need support and time to come together to identify what *they* want to raise, challenge or change;
- any consultation approach should try to ensure that everyone has their say;
- consultation methods need to be sensitive to people's circumstances (e.g. having to identify themselves as receiving support for something others condemn, such as HIV/AIDS).[82]

Preparing for consultation

The following list of hints has been suggested by the Wiltshire Voluntary Development Forum:

- allocate enough resources to be able to complete the exercise (e.g. staff time; budgets for venues, materials and participants' expenses; time and resources for reporting back to participants);

---

81. Richard Byng quoted in Neve (nd), p 9.
82. Wiltshire Voluntary Development Forum (nd) (adapted).

- allow enough time and resource to publicise the consultation and take local advice on when and where to do so;
- decide what information needs to be available and ensure that it is available in appropriate forms (e.g. tape, Braille, Makaton);
- ensure that the process will encourage participation (e.g. choose appropriate venues; find ways to consult those who cannot attend, such as a questionnaire; consider the needs of those who will attend, such as transport, crèche, sitting service);
- allow enough time for people to respond and offer time to discuss the purpose and details;
- provide consultation opportunities for the full range of people you wish to consult;
- make sure that you do not duplicate other consultations.[83]

Needs assessment in general practices

In this example, three general practices worked together to survey the needs of women aged over 40 years who provide informal care for dependants. By working together, they were able to share the resources needed and the work to be done, but were still free to decide at practice level what action they would take once the assessment was completed. The project involved as many practice staff as possible and used a combination of individual practice and joint practice workshops as follows.

Workshop 1. Individual practices (with facilitation) worked on the first stages of needs identification, including looking at the data that they had and the data that they would need to collect.

Workshop 2. Individual practices continued with a more detailed look at health needs in the practice population, concluding by identifying three priorities for health need assessment to take to the third workshop.

Workshop 3. At this workshop, the practices came together to prioritise the nine topics from the previous workshops. Criteria were developed, with the overarching constraint of the need to have a common focus across the three practices. This led to the practices selecting women's mental health as the topic to take forward. Within this topic, each practice was free to concentrate on a group of women of its choice.

Survey. The practices devised a survey with the aid of a research worker. This consisted of a questionnaire to a sample of women and in-depth interviews with ten women from each practice.

cont.

---

83. Wiltshire Voluntary Development Forum (nd) (adapted).

○ ○

Needs assessment in general practices *cont.*

Option appraisal. A final set of workshops appraised the options for action. This included reviewing the resources available to the practices and the external resources. To identify the external resources, the workshops included representatives from local organisations, such as the social services and Age Concern.[84]

○ ○

A multi-method consultation

It was proposed to establish a city health resource centre in the Benwell Shopping Centre, Newcastle. Given that no model for such a centre was available, a multi-stage, multi-method consultation was used, gradually refining a view of what the centre might be like. The methods used included:

❑   awareness-raising through a press launch and the distribution of posters and leaflets in English and Bengali;

❑   every household in the local ward was informed of the study;

❑   a street survey using a self-completed questionnaire;

❑   visits to 23 local groups;

❑   workshops for local residents, arranged in association with local groups;

❑   focus groups and workshops on the detail of a centre;

❑   visits by local people to existing facilities (e.g. a health information shop).[85]

84. University of Salford 1994.
85. Dowswell T, Drinkwater C and Morley V 1994.

○ ○

Needs assessment for locality purchasing

The Salford Locality Health Needs Assessment Project used a five-stage process to involve local people in the commissioning process:

❑   needs identification;

❑   agreement on outcomes;

❑   option generation;

❑   option appraisal;

❑   strategy formulation.

The needs identification stage combined desk research of available data with a questionnaire survey of local people in the groups under review (older people and young men). These were reached through the networks and contacts of members of the task groups (one for each of the two population groups). Client focus groups were also used and felt to be important in gaining ownership of the information.

The task groups generated health outcomes from the research results, producing a wider range of outcomes than had previously been generated at district level when looking at the same problems.

Together, local workers and project workers then identified 80 options for achieving these outcomes. Initially workers' professional views restrained the list of options, but facilitation helped produce a longer, more creative list.

The outcomes were evaluated by the groups against the following criteria, giving most weight to local people's views:

❑   consistency with the views of older people/young men;

❑   consistency with local workers' views;

❑   value for money;

❑   feasibility;

❑   consistency with the priorities of relevant organisations;

❑   promotion of equity;

❑   consistency with GPs' priorities;

❑   evidence of effectiveness.

cont.

○ ○

Needs assessment for locality purchasing *cont.*

The project workers finally drafted a strategy document for each of the two topics.

This project had been set up to explore how needs assessment could both involve local people and contribute to decision making in the relevant local organisations. (Previous evidence had suggested that purchasing plans had not been influenced by needs assessment exercises.) The project concluded that, to be effective, such information needed to be:

❑ timed to feed into the annual planning process (but this was different for the various organisations);

❑ consistent with the organisation's priorities;

❑ produced in a clear report with a summary;

❑ relevant to the organisations' core purpose;

❑ presented through the organisation's existing procedures and fora.[86]

Building alliances

Community development involves building alliances with organisations in the community. Reviewing their work, Health Promotion Wales identified two elements for success: (a) locating the resources in the community and (b) developing alliances. Of alliances, they concluded:

> 'This involves commitment at three levels – the community, at professional level, and among policy makers – to achieve sustained action.
>
> Multi-agency working is central to the task of building healthy alliances. So too is the ability to focus on an aspect of work on which all partners agree.'[87]

ISSUES ISSUES ISSUES ISSUES ISSUES ISSUES ISSUES ISSUES ISSUES

The above rationale for multi-agency working may suggest that only issues common to all the agencies can be tackled.

How would this affect what you wish to do in your area?

---

86. Cohen Z *et al.* 1994.
87. Health Promotion Wales 1995.

4.6 Resources and funding

Progress reports on community development projects repeatedly stress the need for appropriate resourcing. For example:

> 'This health needs assessment was successful because of the resources allocated to it and the commitment of the people involved at different levels.'[88]

> 'The resource implications of rolling-out locality health needs assessment are substantial. We have estimated the cost of the project as approximately £45,000 ... [the cost] would have to be justified in terms of the added value that it would bring to the commissioning process.'[89]

Most projects seem to require fund-raising in addition to the resources of the participating groups and organisations. The sources that have been tapped by previous projects include:

- public health departments;
- primary care development money;
- sponsorship;
- charitable trusts;
- local authorities;
- health authorities;
- trusts;
- European Union;
- joint finance;
- charitable trusts;
- fundholding;
- locality planning teams.

One of the benefits of multi-agency working is that ideas and contacts for funding are pooled. Also, different aspects of the same project may be funded from different sources with, say, a health source and a community source.

88. Webster G and Smithies J 1994, p 3.
89. Cohen Z et al. 1994, p 13.

Health authorities' funding

FHSAs had money available for service development in primary care, and it used to be possible to use this money for community development projects. For example, Camden and Islington FHSA funded a scheme (Manor Gardens Centre) to lend accident prevention equipment to low income families and the City and East London FHSA funded a Primary Care Users Information project in Tower Hamlets.[90]

Health Commission funds might be accessed in the same way.

4.7 Publications

The role of information in empowerment has already been discussed above. Given that community development emphasises relating health activities to the needs and situations of communities and involving the community, it is not surprising that some workers have made the case for locally produced health information publications.[91] The following guidelines have been suggested for those developing health education publications with a community development emphasis:

- make sure the publication meets user need rather than just professional interest;
- check similar work. Can you use it? Can you build on it?;
- find out as much as possible about the target audience's needs. Use community development methods to involve the community in defining these needs;
- find out the target audience's current knowledge and attitudes on the subject;
- make sure that you meet the audience's needs, checking the appropriate length, depth and language level with the audience;
- include community actions as well as individual actions in the advice;
- ensure that the design and appearance meet expectations. A professional designer with knowledge of the target audience can help here. Local colleges can often help here;
- are other formats needed (e.g. Braille, translations)?;
- involve the target audience in evaluating the publication.[92]

90. Russell J 1995, p 42.
91. Farrant W and Russell J 1985 quoted in Leyden R, Martins M and Russell J 1994, p 33.
92. Leyden R, Martins M and Russell J 1994, pp 41–43 (adapted).

ISSUES ISSUES ISSUES ISSUES ISSUES ISSUES ISSUES ISSUES ISSUES

Will your team's initiative require the production of information materials?

If it will, who will:

- decide the content?

- write them?

- test them?

- design and produce them?

What is the role of participation in this?

○ ○

Community development of menopause publications

In this project, professional workers drafted materials with local women's groups which then helped with testing the materials. The project arose because the standard materials then available where too expensive to distribute to the women who needed them and did not include local information.

There were initial problems in getting the materials into a form that would appeal to the target audience. This problem was solved by using a designer with experience of working with community groups. 'She had detailed discussions with women's groups about the format, colours, type of paper and overall look of the materials. The final booklets were very different as a result of this.'

The project workers concluded:

Producing materials with full community participation has resulted in materials which are different from the bulk of the nationally-produced materials carried by Lothian Health Promotion Department. They are more detailed, contain much local information – and humour – and are less glossy. They are likely to be more effective because they respond to what women want.'

'Equally as important was the process of producing them. It influenced local services, gave value to local women's opinions about health education materials, and we hope, will encourage them to look critically at health education materials in the future.[93]

---

93. Sim J, Moffat S and Menzies F 1994, pp 45–46.

4.8 The role of community groups

The philosophy behind community development assumes that both to identify needs and to meet them effectively needs the active participation of the community. This can result in community groups taking key roles in almost any aspect of a project, including:

- developing the initial proposal;
- fundraising;
- finding the participating groups and organisations;
- planning and executing needs surveys involving local people;
- running services;
- evaluating the project;
- lobbying.

○ ○

Limeside Project groups

In the Limeside Project, groups were involved in:

❏   identifying the broad health needs which then shaped the questionnaire;

❏   designing the questionnaire through commenting on the questions and piloting;

❏   training for and interviewing individuals (24 individuals carried out over 200 interviews);

❏   deciding which groups and individuals should be interviewed and by what method;

❏   the analysis, through commenting on the findings and shaping the recommendations.[94]

○ ○

Mid-Glamorgan group involvement

In the Mid-Glamorgan project (see Chapter 6), the local women helped run the house and the events provided in and around it.

---

94. Webster G and Smithies J 1994, p 11.

○ ○

Self-help groups at Wells Park

Self-help groups at Wells Park included:

❏ slimming groups;

❏ parents and toddlers groups;

❏ reminiscence groups for elderly people;

❏ a group for people with irritable bowel syndrome;

❏ a group for people who are HIV positive;

❏ a support group for people with mental health needs;

❏ a herbal health group.[95]

ISSUES ISSUES ISSUES ISSUES ISSUES ISSUES ISSUES ISSUES ISSUES

What do you see as the role of community groups in the initiative?

Do the community workers take the same view?

Encouraging individual and group participation

However desirable the involvement of individuals and groups may be, and however much they would like to be involved, they may still be hesitant in offering their help. After all, some of those who most need to be involved (because their needs are the least met) are also those who have the least confidence in their abilities and most are in awe of professionals. For these reasons, many community development projects have taken special steps to encourage involvement. These include:

- paying expenses (e.g. for interviewing);
- training sessions in participation;
- providing crèches and sitting services for carers;
- providing interpreting facilities;
- putting notices and leaflets in plain English and relevant languages;
- involving people within their own groups;
- using locally accessible venues (e.g. for workshops and meetings);
- using specific strategies for groups who are hard to reach.

---

95. Russell J 1995, p 26.

ISSUES ISSUES ISSUES ISSUES ISSUES ISSUES ISSUES ISSUES ISSUES

What reasons might people in your locality have for not becoming involved in a project?

What steps might the initiative take to make itself more accessible to such people?

4.9 The role of the community worker

Projects can be staffed in many different ways and can be based in various centres (e.g. PHCT, the community, a trust hospital, or health authority). However, there is evidence that the active involvement of a community worker can be instrumental in a successful project and can speed up access to community resources. The Limehouse Project concluded that the community worker had:

- provided easy access to a wide range of individuals;
- knew, and could tap into, community networks;
- created a healthy alliance of local organisations (e.g. gaining access to a primary school for interview rooms;
- provided a trusted link which encouraged residents to become involved;
- supported local people as they worked on the project;
- knew the location of community resources and had provided access to them.[96]

ISSUES ISSUES ISSUES ISSUES ISSUES ISSUES ISSUES ISSUES ISSUES

You might make a list of what you see as the key contributions that community workers can bring to the initiative and what you see as the PHCT's key contributions.

Asking the community workers to do the same and then exchanging lists can be helpful in clarifying roles.

4.10 The role of the working group

Most projects are multi-agency and so bring problems of management and co-ordination. These are usually resolved through a project or working group consisting of representatives of the main agencies and the community.

---

96. Webster G and Smithies J 1994, p 18.

○ ○

The Limehouse Project working group

Membership

❏   District Health Promotion Officer

❏   CHC Secretary

❏   Community Development and Health Worker

❏   Public Health Resource Centre Worker

❏   Nursing/Quality Adviser.

ISSUES ISSUES ISSUES ISSUES ISSUES ISSUES ISSUES ISSUES ISSUES

How will the initiative be managed?

Will it need a steering group?

Will it need a working group?

How can you equip local people to become confident about being involved?

4.11 Timescales

Many accounts of community projects emphasise their long-term nature and the need to avoid anticipating quick results. Nevertheless, projects of just a few months can be useful (e.g. patient satisfaction surveys), although others may take years to come to fruition. What can be expected within any given timescale is summarised in Figure 10.

By choosing a mixture of activities with different timescales, it is possible to both pursue long-term goals and achieve some short-term results. The latter can be important in maintaining participants' enthusiasm and in persuading funders and others that their continued support is worthwhile.

Timescale	Typically	Examples of feasible projects
Long-term	3 years	Work on values, priorities, etc. as part of a consumer education/social marketing strategy
Medium-term	1–3 years	Community health projects; work on evaluating outcomes; community-based needs assessment
Short-term	1 year	Rapid appraisal, consulting with local organisations which are already structured for involvement (e.g. community health councils)
Immediate	1–2 months	Patient satisfaction surveys

Figure 10 Timescales and typical projects[97]

ISSUES ISSUES ISSUES ISSUES ISSUES ISSUES ISSUES ISSUES ISSUES

What timescale do you have in mind?

What pressures are there to show short-term results?

Which goals are only achievable in the long term?

Can the project design encompass both short- and long-term goals?

97. Labyrinth Training (adapted) – unpublished materials.

Chapter 5

Developing and accessing skills

5.1 Skills needed by health and community workers

Many of the ideas and methods in community development will be new to general practice and other health staff. The conventional ways of working, focused on the practice list and on the individual patient and emphasising professional control of health knowledge, are all challenged by community methods.[98]

The skills needed to carry out community development depend to some extent on the nature of the project. Who needs the skills (and especially which skills are needed by health staff and which by community workers) depends on how tasks are shared between the workers and between the organisations. One list of skills and knowledge for community workers is given below. Sometimes some of these skills might be needed by health workers:

- research;
- information skills;
- information technology skills;
- analytical skills;
- interpersonal skills;
- motivational skills;
- education and training skills;
- group work skills;
- listening and communication skills;
- knowledge of organisational theory and practice;
- financial and book-keeping skills;
- knowledge of how government and business work;
- management skills;
- negotiation skills;
- brokerage skills;
- lobbying skills;
- knowledge of relevant legislation.[99]

---

98. Brown I 1994.
99. Taylor M 1992, p 9 (adapted).

This list demonstrates the impracticality of one person hoping to have all the knowledge and skills needed for community development. Rather, it emphasises the importance of a project having access to this range of skills and knowledge and the importance of multi-agency working in helping to provide such skills.

Another approach to training community workers distinguishes the core skills (needed by all community workers) and those optional skills that may be needed by selected workers.[100] In this system, the core and options are as shown in Table 6.

Table 6 Core and optional knowledge and skills

Core knowledge and skills	Optional knowledge and skills
• an awareness of where participants are starting from and their expectations of community work • what community work is • powerlessness and empowerment	• how to start a community group • how groups function • networking • publicity and campaigning • influencing decisions • fund-raising

ISSUES ISSUES ISSUES ISSUES ISSUES ISSUES ISSUES ISSUES ISSUES

What skills will your team's initiative need?

Where will the skills come from?

5.2 Skills needed by the community

The WHO study group identified a range of skills which it felt had to exist in the community if it is 'to become an equal partner with the health services'. These skills came under four broad headings: speaking the language of the health system; community understanding; using communications channels; and other possible needs. The more specific skills under each heading are listed in Table 7.

100. Federation of Community Work Training Groups, 1992.

Table 7 Skills needed in the community[101]

Skill area	Detailed skills
Speaking the language of the health system	• familiarity with health vocabulary and concepts • knowledge of the local health system, including its priorities and programmes • knowledge of what other sectors can offer in terms of promoting better health
Community understanding	• achieving a consensus on health needs • formulating ideas and public speaking • managing community meetings • handling conflicts with the health services
Using communication channels	• intercommunication between the community and the health service • participating in informal and formal meetings • where appropriate (e.g. for conducting surveys), use of the telephone
Other possible needs	• internal organisation of the community • analysing and evaluating health action • continuous questioning and examination of health issues

5.3 Training methods for community workers

Community development emphasises the need for people to be involved in decisions which affect them. This philosophy is reflected in the training of community workers which uses participatory learning methods. (Some texts prefer the term 'active learning'.)

Participatory methods are based on theories of adult learning such as those surveyed by Knowles.[102] These theories emphasise the characteristics of adult learning (see column 1 of Table 8). Column 2 of the table identifies some of the implications of these characteristics for the planning of courses for adult learners.

---

101. World Health Organization 1991, p 35 (adapted).
102. Knowles 1975 and 1990.

Table 8 Adult learning theories and their implications for course design[103]

Aspect of adult learning	Implications for training courses
Adults are self-directing	• need accepting, comfortable environment • learning outcomes should be negotiated • participants should be involved in planning the course • the teaching and learning style should emphasise mutual responsibility for the process • evaluation and assessment should involve the participants
Adults bring their rich experience to the course	• the course should promote the sharing of this experience • the new learning should be related to this experience • the experience may make the participants less open to new ideas
Adults learning is affected by their past roles	• courses need to help adults reflect on this
Adults prefer a problem-centred approach to learning rather than a subject-centred one	• the course should help the participants to articulate the problems which interest them • the course should help participants explore solutions to these problems

The practical application of these principles to the training of community workers can be seen in the approach taken by the Federation of Community Work Training Groups with their emphasis on:

- courses being led by facilitators rather than trainers;
- the use of participants' experience;
- the use of active small group methods such as buzz groups, brain-storming, role play and case studies;
- personal project work.

The Federation's suggested programme appears in Figure 11. Samples of other training programmes can be found in Association of Metropolitan Authorities (1990).

---

103. Based on Henderson 1989, pp 4–5.

Community work training programme

Session 1: Introduction

- participants and facilitators begin to get to know each other
- facilitators describe course aims and methods
- the course content is negotiated

Session 2: What is community work?

- participants begin to share their experience and identify what for them are key components of community work
- inputs on how others have defined community work

Sessions 3 and 4: Powerlessness and empowerment

- the exploration of power and powerlessness both from personal experience and from an institutional perspective

Sessions 5–9: Developing community work skills and knowledge

- starting a community group
- how groups function
- networking
- publicity
- influencing decisions
- fund-raising

Session 10: Evaluation

- participants evaluate their own learning, the course and their future needs.

Figure 11 A typical community work training programme[104]

---

104. Federation of Community Work Training Groups 1992, p 17.

○ ○

A training day for community development workers in Bromley

Aims

To provide an overview of current community development provision in the borough and to develop a co-ordinated approach to the promotion of community development in Bromley.

Objectives

❑ to provide an opportunity for networking

❑ to explore issues and approaches to community development work

❑ to share constraints and opportunities for the development of the work

❑ to begin to develop a strategy for community development in Bromley.

Programme: 10.00 am to 4.00 pm

Session 1
Mapping exercise. Participants will describe the aims and objectives of their own project, its funding source, groups involved in the work and the methods they use to involve the community.

Session 2
Participants will identify what is going well in their work and what the constraints are.

Session 3
In this session participants will explore the opportunities that may exist to develop their work. Taking on board issues such as assessing need, developing a work programme and prioritising work.

Lunch

Session 4
Participants will explore the different levels involved in community work and identify where they are on the spectrum. They will explore effective approaches for developing their work at different levels.

Session 5
Participants will explore what structures and support they need to enable them to work more effectively as a group to inform policy development and service delivery in Bromley.[105]

---

105. Programme supplied by Helen Naylor.

5.4 Standards and qualifications

A number of qualifications (e.g. university certificates and diplomas) exist for community work. Potentially, though, the new Scottish/National Vocational Qualifications (S/NVQs) will set the standards for work in community development. The standards are divided into six key roles:

A Engage with communities and establish agreements for involvement
B Enable people to work and learn together effectively
C Enable people in communities to identify needs and rights and plan action
D Enable communities and community groups to take and review collective action
E Provide organisational support to collective action
F Contribute to the development of own and organisation's work.

Further details of the standards and the qualifications being developed from them can be obtained from: Federation of Community Work Training Groups; CCETSW; City and Guilds; and SCOTVEC. The addresses of these organisations are given in Appendix 2.

5.5 Training resources

See Appendix 2.

Chapter 6

Case studies

6.1 A community health house

This project in Mid-Glamorgan set out to explore what community-based health visiting might look like.[106] The area covered by the project was poor and largely consisted of council houses. There was little sense of community.

At the centre of the project was a leased house which was used as a drop-in centre for women on the estate. Professional support was provided by a health visitor and a nursery nurse who ran a crèche in the house. Many other professionals took part in various aspects of the house, e.g. a psychiatric nurse and adult education tutors. The project's activities were decided through discussion by those attending and included:

* shared shopping followed by preparing lunch;
* trips (e.g. swimming);
* courses run by health professionals (e.g. first aid, talking about feelings, ante- and post-natal care, children's illnesses, nutrition and cooking, and hobbies and crafts);
* social activities, e.g. strawberry picking and a barbecue;
* fund-raising events (e.g. jumble sales).

Fewer women were seen by the health visitor at the house than would have been seen in home visits but 'the opportunities for effecting real behaviour change were much greater.'

6.2 Rhymney Valley Better Health Initiative

This project carried out a health survey in an area with a population of 21,000. Much use was made of published data but this was supplemented by meetings with local organisations (e.g. the community council), by in-depth interviews and by market research.

---

106. Bryar R and Fisk L 1994.

The survey identified 15 priority areas, including:

- develop a community-based multi-agency approach dealing with all aspects of ageing;
- develop a substance misuse programme;
- work closely with community education, youth and leisure services to emphasise the benefits of safe exercise and accessible leisure and recreation services;
- provide training and support to deal with aggression, stress, and behavioural difficulties among children and the family;
- work with others to tackle the problem of dog fouling;
- establish a community forum to monitor the health implications of local policy and planning;
- appoint a multi-funded community worker with a wide remit, influence and credibility.[107]

The following lessons were learnt from the initiative:

- be realistic about what can be achieved, the scope of any project developed, and the level of commitment required of partners in the community;
- be specific about areas of action. Realistic objectives and specific targeting of achievable projects should bring results which encourage further action;
- communicate at all stages with those helping with, and working on, the project. Use the media as much as possible;
- be aware of changing priorities. A community is evolving and its needs change;
- appreciate the pace of the community, and its formal and informal structures. Recognise that some things, such as gaining local authority approval, take time but can result in powerful effort;
- remember that ethical considerations and the need for confidentiality should always underpin work with communities. Working *on* a community may be regarded as manipulation, working *for* a community can be seen as a service, but working *with* a community will lead to real partnership.[108]

---

107. Health Promotion Wales 1995.
108. Health Promotion Wales 1995.

6.3 Heeley Health Project*

In many ways, Heeley is a microcosm of Sheffield and its health experience mirrors that of the whole city. While there are pockets of comparative affluence, there are also areas of real deprivation. This has been highlighted by Colin Thunhurst (1985), in his study of poverty and health in Sheffield. Sections of the population in Heeley with considerable health needs include elderly people, single parent families, those with low incomes and some minority ethnic communities.

The Heeley Health Project was born out of discussions between local community workers, GPs and other staff from the Heeley Green surgery. They had a commitment to viewing health in broad terms and finding positive ways to improve health and well being, rather than merely treating patients for illness. It was also seen as important to target those sectors of the population most in need, and to involve them in maintaining and improving their own health.

Before the project started, local community workers had begun to address a range of health-related issues. The Heeley Green surgery already supported a pensioners lunch club and parents' group; and provided a well woman clinic and health information library. Staff at the surgery had developed good links with the local community. In addition, there were already a number of well-established groups and activities in Heeley.

Setting up the health project

Initially, a planning group of local workers proposed a month of activities, aimed at promoting positive health, and the establishment of some new groups. However, in the light of other projects' experience, it was recognised that a longer-term initiative was needed in order to effect any real change.

Funding was sought and obtained from the FHSA, initially for one year. This provided 70 per cent of salary costs for one project worker. The additional salary costs, plus some running costs, were provided by Healthy Sheffield 2000. Further funding was subsequently obtained from the FHSA and Healthy Sheffield, which runs until April 1994. Funding for the project's continuation after this date is being pursued from a number of sources.

---

* This section is reproduced by kind permission from Chaplin J 1992.

Additional funding has been received through the FHSA for activities which meet the requirements of health promotion 'clinics', for example a food issues group and an Agewell group.

The Project Worker, Jenny River, took up her post on 31 March 1990 – the day before the NHS changes took effect. Having trained as a nurse, Jenny spent the previous 12 years working in adult education, teaching and working with groups. Jenny felt excited by the challenge of developing the Heeley Health Project, as it provided an opportunity 'To work on issues that were important to me; and to give me the change to use my experience, and work in ways that I feel are most effective'.

Location

The project is based at Heeley Green Community Centre, a building which has both good access and a lovely garden, shared with the GP surgery. The building also houses the Heeley Advice Centre and local community workers. It is situated in a small but busy shopping centre and provides the base for a wide range of activities, including some organised through the health project. Project activities also take place at the nearby Heeley Bank Community Rooms; which provide the only real creche facility in the area; the Youth and Community Centre and other venues such as church halls and school premises.

Relationship with Heeley Green surgery

As the project is independent it involves people from the whole of Heeley. However, it has strong and valuable links with the Heeley Green practice. Health workers were crucial in establishing the project and staff support it in many ways. Some are members of the project's Management Committee, while a number of joint developments have taken place, including a breast screening video and an HIV/AIDS awareness week. The Practice Nurse contributes to groups such as Agewell; the Practice Counsellor facilitated a Prime of Life group for women; while other staff have been involved in health days.

Management

Initially, the Management Committee was composed of those involved in setting it up, plus a researcher from the Community Operational Research Unit, who helps to evaluate the project. As part of the project's commitment to participation by the local community at all levels, including management, a user group was set up. This is open to anyone attending current project activities and is a forum where members of different groups share their experiences and ideas, raise issues which concern them and discuss and initiate new developments, as well as the project's overall direction. The long-term aim is to involve people from the user group in the management of the project and this is underway, with sessions planned to increase confidence and understanding. The current Management Committee recognises that the style of meetings may need to change and that considerations such as childcare needs will have to be taken into account.

Making links

One of the Projects Worker's first tasks was to make links with existing local, city-wide and national networks. Important relationships were developed early on with other voluntary organisations and health projects; Healthy Sheffield 2000 (HS2000); the local authority Health and Consumer Services; and the health authority Health Promotion Department. HS2000, as part of the national and international Healthy Cities Network, provides a link and develops joint initiatives between the local authority, health authority and voluntary sector.

At local level this process was vital in finding out what was already being done in the area, in identifying health needs and concerns, and linking these with a wider perspective. From a number of meetings held with groups and individuals it became clear that many people were already linked into local networks and activities. However, a number of isolated groups and individuals were less well-integrated into the community.

A long list of health concerns was then compiled, categorised under a broad range of headings. Some concerns were specific to particular groups, such as access to buildings for people with disabilities, while others were common to many groups, for example the cost of 'healthy' food. Local people also indicated what kinds of activities they might be involved in.

Groups and activities

The next stage was to make decisions about where to start, from the list of health concerns and issues raised. The Management Committee felt that developments should be those which could be achieved within a short time; and could be sustained by local people if the project were to close after the first year. Some issues and ideas which appeared a number of times were tried out at a health day held in July 1990. This day aroused considerable enthusiasm, and the first groups were established that autumn.

Agewell

Heeley has a high elderly population, for whom isolation, decreasing mobility, low income and lack of company feature highly. The 1990 Agewell Festival was the inspiration for a Heeley group and meetings began in October 1990. The group has a regular attendance, with tasks shared out among members. Popular sessions have included: relaxation; herbal remedies; cooking for one; patients' rights; and chiropody. Group members also led a discussion at the 1991 Agewell Festival and organised a Health Day for Older People last July. This group is currently working with the Theatreworks team to produce a short piece of theatre about issues relevant to older adults.

Food issues group

This was set up in response to concerns about: the cost and availability of food, particularly 'healthy' food; food additives; how to get children to eat properly; and the effects of modern farming techniques. Initially, the group concentrated on becoming better informed about these issues. Group members also took part in a Health Education Authority research project. Other activities include a food audit, to find out about food available locally and to compare the prices of standard items with healthier alternatives; and a healthy picnic for local residents.

Health and Environment Branch of WEA

The project found that a number of residents wanted the opportunity to develop their skills and understanding of certain topics. Despite cuts in community education, the Workers Education Association was continuing to fund courses at the Heeley City Farm, including: gardening; backyard farming; and environmental issues.

Negotiations between the project, the WEA and the City Farm resulted in the establishment of the Health and Environment Branch.

Course have continued to be developed around the farm, while on the 'health' side, courses have included: women's health; relaxation; herbal health; assertiveness and confidence building; women's self-defence; and wholefood cookery. These have been well-attended, mainly by local residents. Close links between these courses and other health project activities have led to developments such as the mother and baby group.

Support groups

Early in 1991, the project established several support groups. These provide an opportunity for people in similar circumstances to meet, share experiences, and gain confidence and support. A group for mothers of children with special needs started at the suggestion of a local mother, who developed the idea and made contact with others. Support was provided by the Project Worker and a social worker.

Another resident's idea led to a support group for those who are anxious, depressed, isolated or lonely. This group is supported by the Project Worker and an occupational therapist.

The Mother and Baby Group developed out of concern by health visitors, midwives and local women about the pressures on mothers – particularly young and first-time mothers – and their potential isolation. Two project users, both mothers of young children, expressed an interest in setting up this group. It is used mainly by young mothers who are not yet part of the existing network of women's and children's activities.

The Prime of Life Group was developed and facilitated by the Heeley Green Practice Counsellor. It focused on the physical, emotional and social aspects of mid-life, often seen as a difficult period when growing older is viewed negatively. This group looked at such topics as children, parents, the menopause, relationships, health and ageing.

Health Days and other events

Nearly 200 people attended the Heeley Health Day, which was a public launch for the project in July 1990. It provided a number of activities, as well as free healthy food. By the end of the day about 80 people had indicated an interest in further involvement, which gave the project the go-ahead to organise the most popular activities.

Two women's Health Days were held in March 1991, to celebrate International Women's Day. These provided an opportunity for women to try out new activities and discuss relevant issues, in a friendly and informal environment. The first was a lunchtime event with food, music and live theatre. 'Don't Call Me Brave' showed a women with breast cancer, struggling with the disease and the doctors, which was followed by group discussion. The second day provided a wide range of activities, as well as food, music and discussion. Both events attracted a lot of women and children.

An evening event on the NHS changes provided the opportunity for some lively debate. A local GP led a discussion about the effects of changes on patient care in general practice, while the Theatreworks group provided an entertaining performance about the NHS. The local pharmacist and his pop group had everyone dancing by the end of the evening.

Community shop

The project also contributed towards setting up a community shop on the St Elizabeth's Close estate. The project worker and the nutritionist from Health and Consumer Services were involved with the community group and the housing development worker, in obtaining funding and developing the project. The shop opened in June 1991 and sells a range of popular basic foods, household goods and some fruit and vegetables. A wider range of 'healthier' alternatives is gradually being introduced, to complement more standard items.

The community group carried out a survey in advance. They staff the shop on a voluntary basis and do all the work involved in running it, with support from the estate's housing development worker. The health project worker and community group are currently developing plans for cookery sessions, based on ingredients which will he sold in the shop.

Breast screening video

The breast screening programme for women aged 50–65 has begun in Sheffield and women are being called for mammography. A Heeley Green GP, involved with the Open University, was keen to make a film to show the concerns and anxieties of women called up for this procedure.

Four women patients from the practice participated in the film and the GP, practice nurse, practice counsellor and health project worker took part. Both practice and project learnt a great deal from this experience, and are now looking at ways of providing support for women undergoing breast screening in future. The women who took part felt strongly that mutual support was vital and have offered to be involved.

HIV/AIDS awareness week

This involved Heeley Green and another surgery, the Health Project, Sheffield AIDS Education Project and the local chemist working together to raise awareness, provide information and counter mis-information. Training sessions were held for workers before the event.

Exhibitions were put up in the surgery, community centres and chemists, providing information and inviting people to discuss their concerns. In the surgeries, patients had an opportunity to discuss the issues with a nurse or GP. Groups organised through the Health Project held discussions. The response from the local community was positive: most people welcomed the chance to talk and felt it was good to have accessible information.

Additional activities

During its second year, the project has consolidated much of the initial work and groups and activities have continued to grow and develop. These include a Tai Chi group, which attracts both men and women in a mixed age range; and circle dancing, which is attended mainly by older women. Both groups developed as spin-offs from other events and are now an established part of the programme. A swimming group has started, in response to demand from Agewell group members. It is organised in conjunction with the Recreation Department, which provides transport and a reduced entry fee. As well as older women, this group also appeals to young mothers.

A recent development is a Wednesday open morning. This is a drop-in which offers the opportunity to meet and exchange information over a cup of coffee. Health books are available on loan, plus other information and there are toys for children to play with. The group attracts a wide mix of people, including regulars' who are important in encouraging new people to become involved in activities. Other local workers are starting to use the group as a contact point. Free herbal health/dietary advice consultations by a local herbalist have just started, due to popular demand.

Future plans

Funding has now been secured to April 1994, with salary costs being met by the FHSA and HS2000 (via the Urban Programme). Additional funding has also been received from Trent RHA, for development work with groups and to extend the project's work around food. Some smaller amounts of funding have also been received.

Future plans include following up the Food Audit by working with local retailers, linked with food events such as cookery demonstrations and tastings; liaison with schools and other agencies; starting a communal allotment; using the Food Show currently being prepared by Theatreworks to stimulate discussion; and producing an exhibition about food issues and local activities.

Short courses in basic counselling skills and group skills are planned in response to local interest, with the aim of demystifying these techniques and help people offer support to each other. A day and evening of activities are planned for International Women's Day, including a show by Yorkshire Women's Theatre Group about women and alcohol, entitled 'Under the Table'. Childcare provision is a big issue locally – particularly after-school care – and the project hopes to he involved with the local community worker in responding to this.

Other high priority issues in the community include road safety and public transport. Mental health and stress are also key issues and the project hopes to convene a meeting between workers from relevant agencies, to look at ways of responding.

Support from the FHSA

Without substantial support from the FHSA in funding the community health worker post, it is unlikely that the project would have been established. In addition, this has made it much easier to attract funding from elsewhere. The project feels that the FHSA has shown real commitment by this initiative, as it has been able to demonstrate the important role of community health projects in complementing health promotion activities carried out in GP surgeries.

6.4 Wells Park Health Project[109]

Background

The Wells Park Health Project is a community development organisation. It was founded in 1984 and works closely with, but is organisationally and financially separate from, the Wells Park Practice. Funding originally came from charitable sources, but since 1991 the FHSA has been the main funder of the project. The project is a charity, managed by a committee of local people and professionals, including a nurse and a GP from the practice.

Staffing

The staff consists of two full-time community workers, one administrative worker and one part-time attached community work student.

Aims

- To provide services, within the capacity of the project, responding to local need
- To develop needs assessment from a lay point of view, with an emphasis on ethnic minority work
- To develop a methodology that will fuse qualitative, action-oriented community development with a more rigorous research-based approach
- To find a way to use the information gained to influence purchasing decisions of the health commission
- To continue to involve local people in running and determining the direction of the project.

Activities

The project has a wide range of activities, including the following.

Advice and advocacy

This offers welfare rights advice and associated advocacy within a community development framework. Its goal is to help maximise the benefits that clients might be entitled to.

---

109. Wells Park Health Project 1996.

Counselling

Three of the project workers provide counselling services to local people.

Elderflower group

This is a group for black people who are over 50 years of age. It seeks to meet their social, emotional and mental needs. Many of the members have suffered the effects of isolation and are diabetic, arthritic or coping with the menopause. Members develop their own programmes and engage in arts, crafts and a variety of workshops.

Joint housing welfare work

This work tackles the link between ill health and bad housing by building links between local housing workers, the project and the practice. The aim is, through better understanding of individual cases, to help solve people's accommodation problems.

Library and equipment loan

This service lends books, leaflets and equipment to local people. Book loans are 31 per cent life skills and 69 per cent medical. Tens machines are available for those with chronic painful conditions.

Other groups

Other groups include: over-50s keep fit; over-50s women's swimming; parents and toddlers; reminiscence; and respect for Asian women.

6.5 Brockenhurst Healthy Village Project

Background

This project was a joint venture between Southampton and South West Hamphsire Health Commission, Wessex Regional Health Authority, Hampshire County Council Education Department and Brockenhurst College. Two villages in the New Forest were involved: Brockenhurst (3,500 population) and Sway (3,000). The staff of the general practice for the area included: four general practitioners, one practice manager, two part-time practice nurses, a community nurse adviser for elderly people, a district nurse, a part-time physiotherapist and a part-time district chiropodist.

The problem

The practice area included considerable deprivation with problems of ill health, poor housing, depression, loneliness, learning difficulties, juvenile problems and stress. The project set out to harness the resources of the community to promote healthy living.

The facilities

The community facilities included a new village hall, a church hall, a community college, leisure facilities at local hotels, a swimming pool, and many local organisations and groups.

Methods

The project appointed a part-time co-ordinator whose work included:

- talking and listening to individuals, encouraging them to complete a health status questionnaire, and advising them about activities and facilities;
- helping to introduce people to those who can help them develop new interests;
- monitoring the progress of those who contacted the project;
- keeping a database of local activities and facilities;
- finding facilities to match particular needs (e.g. finding a meeting place for stroke victims);
- publicising the project.

1 Agree to referral/self-referral
↓
2 Co-ordinator makes contact and visits
↓
3 Activity package
↓
4 Two-week visit by co-ordinator ⟶ Feedback to referee
↓
5 Three-week visit by co-ordinator ⟶ Feedback to referee and back to BHVP
↓
6 Six-month final visit by co-ordinator ⟶ Feedback to referee and back to BHVP

BHVP = Brockenhurst Healthy Village Project

Figure 12 The Brockenhurst referral system[110]

110. Browne D 1994, p 36.

Referrals could come from a GP or be self-referral. The referral system is illustrated in Figure 12.

Results

During a period of 18 months, 41 people were offered contact with the project and 34 took up the offer. Twenty-five people were referred by their GP, three by other practice staff and two were self-referrals. Twenty-two people took up an activity as a result. Tables 9 and 10, based on 30 completed questionnaires, show that there was a high level of satisfaction with the service and a shared view that people's health had improved.

Table 9 Impact of referral on individual goals[111]

	Referrers	per cent	Users	per cent
Been achieved	16	53	17	57
On way to being achieved	11	37	7	23
Not going to be achieved	3	10	6	20

Table 10 Impact of referral on sense of individual well-being and health[112]

	Referrers	per cent	Users	per cent
Improved	20	67	22	73
Remained the same	9	30	6	20
Deteriorated	0	0	2	7
Don't know	1	3	0	0

6.6 Barton, Watcombe and Hele (Torquay) Health Gain Initiative[113]

The Barton, Watcombe and Hele Health Gain Initiative is based on three suburbs in the north of Torquay with a total population of 12,100. The project is led by the health authority.

Origins

The project arose from the concerns of a general practitioner at the Barton Health Centre who approached the health authority about the excessive

---

111. Southampton and South West Hampshire Health Authority 1996.
112. Southampton and South West Hampshire Health Authority 1996.
113. Information provided by Trevor Gay and Meryl Basham, 1996.

demands on the PHCT at the centre. It was felt that these demands were linked to the social deprivation in the area. After discussion, it was agreed that a community health needs assessment should be carried out.

The survey

The survey confirmed that, following the Jarman index, there was a high level of social deprivation in the area when compared to other parts of Torquay and Devon.

In March 1994, the health authority organised a brainstorming session in a local pub. Over 60 people from various statutory and voluntary agencies attended, together with local people and their representatives. Participants were asked to say what they thought the needs in the locality were and to suggest ways in which those needs might be met. Further views were sought at a local social services family centre.

The report

A report based of the discussions was published in June 1994. Following a three-month consultation period, a steering group was set up to develop the proposals in the report. The group was made up of representatives of 12 agencies with the task of deciding how to move the project forward.

The community worker

As a result of the steering group's work, a community worker was appointed in August 1995, funded by the health authority, to work with local people and to address their concerns. The steering group felt that the worker should be managed by a voluntary agency; Torbay Voluntary Service agreed to do this under a contract with the health authority.

Funding and the management of the project

The health authority provides provides a development fund to support the local initiatives managed by the report. A small management group was formed from the larger steering group to handle the detailed aspects of the project. This management group included representatives from Devon social services, Torbay Borough Council officers, Torbay Borough councillors, Community Education, the police, the health centre, Torbay Voluntary Service and the health authority. It had been agreed that three local people should be elected to the group and that this should be one of the first tasks of the community worker.

The management group has agreed its constitution and set itself measurable aims and objectives. The group is accountable to the community forum, which meets twice a year to provide a steering, but non-executive overview of the project. The forum includes all those agencies which have been involved since the beginning of the project, together with other agencies which have joined as work has progressed. There is also an open invitation for local people to attend.

The role of the community worker

The worker, a qualified youth worker, publicised the initiative by:

- talking to local people to find out what facilities were available in the area and to get to know the area;
- using the local media (e.g. publishing articles);
- running three family fun days to promote the initiative, offering circus skills, kite making and games. The local community centres and youth workers were involved in these days and local shops gave support by offering prizes.

The survey

A survey of 100 households was carried out. This was designed to collect background information on the community and was conducted by local people. (The survey was preceded by a session on personal safety and dealing with aggression.) Information was collected on marital status, children, employment and housing, together with people's views on what they feel affects their health, what they think about the services they receive and what their concerns were.

The results showed that the same problems were common to all three areas, including: a lack of policing, the speed of the traffic, vandalism, crime, alcohol and drug misuse, and concerns about young people and their behaviour. This provided the community worker with an agenda to begin work with the local community, reinforced by the aims and objectives of the constitution.

In February 1996, three elected representatives joined the management group and have been expressing the feelings of the community in a powerful and positive way.

Other work

- Productive inter-agency work
- Changes in the way prescriptions for minor conditions (e.g. Calpol) are made, following links with a GP. There is now no need to visit the doctor unless the patient considers it necessary
- A sub-committee of several agencies has been formed to look at how community centre management members are supported and to help them in their responsibilities and accountabilities to the public
- Support was provided to people who wished to start a food co-operative, managed by local people. This is now thriving and planning to expand into other areas
- The survey had shown that people found it difficult to afford leisure facilities, so the development fund has helped to subsidise multi-sports sessions for adults, with a crèche

Many other projects have been supported by grants, including:

- a play bus, to visit areas with no provision for the under-fives;
- a football team, which aims to promote self-esteem in young men;
- a social club for young people;
- a group, with a crèche, for young mothers who need to develop their self-confidence;
- a group for 14-plus young people wishing to become peer educators in their local youth club;
- a summer skills project using basket ball and football (8–11s and 12–15s) and outdoor activities (15–25s);
- support for a detached youth worker.

The initiative's multi-agency approach

The use of a multi-agency approach and the involvement of local people have always been central to the initiative. So far, these aims have been met. At the end of three years, the aim is to enable local people to take over the management of the initiative.

Chapter 7

Evaluating community development

7.1 Why evaluate?

Evaluation has two primary purposes in community development:

- to show what has been achieved (and at what cost);
- to inform future work.

Different stakeholders will place varying emphasis on different aspects of evaluation, as suggested in Table 11.

Table 11 Stakeholders' interests in evaluation [114]

Group	Typical focus of interest
Purchasers	Value for money and health gain
Participants	Ideas for activities
Professionals	Effectiveness of methods

Given that the evaluation of community development is largely qualitative (see below), the starting questions will generally be qualitative:

- what have we been trying to do?
- why have we been trying to do it?
- what is it aiming to achieve?
- how effective has it been?
- who has been involved and at what stages?
- what benefits have we gained from being involved in confidence building? [115]

As listed, these questions tend to emphasise evaluation as an end-of-project activity. This is often the case, but evaluation can be ongoing, collecting data to guide and shape the project as it develops.

114. Laurie E 1994, p 33.
115. Laurie E 1994, p 34 (adapted).

Where community development is used in support of some other health initiative, stakeholders might then bring other, more conventional expectations, to the evaluation. For example, a study of locality purchasing suggested that evaluation should identify the benefits in terms of:

- changes in referral and treatment patterns;
- changes in volume and quality of care;
- improvements in choice for patients;
- better integration of services;
- demonstrable influence of local people on purchasing.[116]

Process and outcome

When evaluating a project, both its processes and its outcomes can be looked at.

Processes refer to what the project did and to its methods. For example, the processes in a community development project include the methods used to collect the data and the methods used to communicate findings to the community.

Outcomes refer to what the project achieved. In a community development project, outcomes might include new services, changes in the use of existing services, or just a greater awareness of people's views.

7.2 Process measures

A community development health project is an interaction of four main strands of activity:

- the environment/community;
- alliances that occur as the project progresses;
- the individual;
- the health services and other agencies.

For any one of these, factors to demonstrate the effects of being involved in the project can be chosen. Such factors might include:

- numbers of people involved in meetings;
- numbers of people contributing to surveys;

116. Bryttan Y 1994, p 5.

- numbers of times groups met;
- numbers using services;
- activities carried out (e.g. a lobby of a local health authority);
- surveys completed;
- staff and others trained;
- attitudes changed;
- networks created;
- skills gained by participants.

One way of evaluating processes is to collect the views of a range of people involved. Spider diagrams can be used for this, as the example in Figure 13 shows. In this case, the labels on the axes were developed for evaluating health alliances, but they can be changed to fit any project, as can the number of axes. Spider diagrams are discussed in more detail in section 7.4.

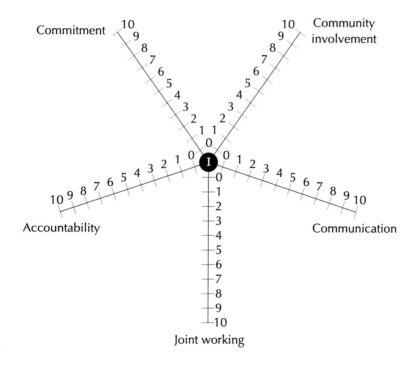

Figure 13 A process evaluation diagram[117]

117. Funnell R, Oldfield K, Speller V 1995, p 51.

Participation measures

Participation may be regarded as a process or an outcome, according to the aims of a particular project so its inclusion here does not contradict its relevance to the section below on outcome measures.

Participation can be measured by using before and after counts of whatever form of activity a project agrees to class as participation. So, participation could be measured by:

- uptake of services;
- involvement in surveys;
- attendance at meetings;

and so on.

7.3 Outcome measures

What counts as an outcome depends on the goals of a particular project. What counts as a useful outcome depends on good sense. In other words, what outcomes can reasonably be expected, and what outcomes would be worth having? The risk in community development health programmes is to set too narrow a range of epidemiologically-based outcomes which could not possibly be achieved on the scale and with the resources of a community project.

Projects need to generate their own outcome measures, ensuring that:

- they are realistic;
- they are observable;
- they are owned by all involved;
- if achieved, would be thought worthwhile.

Effects on primary care services

The outcome effects on primary care services might include:

- changes in uptake;
- services being provided at new locations;
- policy changes;
- new services being offered;

- patients using services more effectively;
- more relevant/usable feedback from patients;
- more effective use of primary care resources;
- greater referrals to other agencies;
- more contact with other agencies;
- more job satisfaction among primary care staff;
- cultural changes (e.g. in professional–patient relationships);
- increase in the use of volunteers.

Effects on agencies

For other agencies, such as social services and community groups, outcome measures might include:

- increase in their level of activity;
- increase in contacts with clients;
- increased/better networking;
- more/better focused referrals to them from other agencies;
- more support or recognition from other bodies;
- more volunteers working with them;
- increase in staff morale;
- increase in staff skills.

Effects on communities

For clarity, the items listed above (under effects on primary care services and effects on agencies) are those which are of exclusive interest to primary care services and agencies. Both primary care services and agencies will be interested in the effects on communities. These might be observable through the following measures.

Service use/facilities change

- Greater or more appropriate use of services
- Greater accessibility of services (e.g. disabled access built)
- Change in profile of users (e.g. more Black people attending)

Other (non-health) facilities change

- New facilities provided (e.g. a play area)

Community participation changes

- More people involved in groups planning or controlling the provision
- More people involved in service provision (e.g. community mothers)
- More lobbying carried out
- Safer environment
- Better knowledge of networks and increased networking

Policy changes

- Policy changes achieved

More fundamentally, though, whatever the community decides is a valued change becomes an evaluation measure.

Effects on health

Generally, community development projects do not expect measurable changes in the health of specific individuals and so do not use traditional epidemiological measures. For example (see box below) one heart health programme looked for increases in facilities and in participation rates, but it did not attempt to measure the health of individuals. The measures in this example could be regarded as proxy measures: if they show an improvement, an improvement in heart health is assumed to follow.

Changes in outcome in community projects tend to be collective measures rather than individual measures, since community development seeks to change the *community*. Individual change is assumed to follow, although perhaps on a long-term basis. The health indicators, therefore, tend to be indicators of health-enhancers rather than of health states. Typical indicators are:

- availability of sport, leisure and recreational facilities;
- change in take-up of health services;
- uptake of sport, leisure and recreational facilities;
- uptake of health services;
- appropriateness of use of health services;
- availability of educational facilities;
- uptake of educational facilities;
- attitudes towards healthy behaviour;

- health awareness (e.g. of safe-sex or alcohol limits);
- policy changes.

Whatever measures are used, they are likely to be based on two sources:

- the original project aims (which will have been agreed with the community);
- community discussion of how the project should be evaluated and which outcomes local people are most keen to see.

○ ○

Outcome measures on a heart health project[118]

Progress was tracked by the systematic recording of the outcome measures such as:

❏ participation rates in health-related action;

❏ physical changes to the environment (e.g. new play area, traffic safety measures);

❏ perceived changes in knowledge, attitude and behaviour of the target population or sub-groups of it;

❏ changes in the availability of health-promoting facilities and resources (e.g. exercise groups).

Outcomes of this project included:

❏ a play park;

❏ new street signs and traffic control;

❏ a new playground at a primary school;

❏ a revamped pub;

❏ an increase in community centre activities from 4 to 18 per week (e.g. over 50s keep fit, aerobics, discos).

The project workers note that '... all these can be reasonably supposed to contribute to a decrease in heart disease risk.'

---

118. Ewles L, Miles U and Velleman G 1995.

Effects on social aspects

As with health measures, the social measures in community development tend to concentrate on the community, on changed facilities and changed use of facilities. These might include:

- more or better housing;
- existence of a community centre;
- activities at a community centre;
- participation in running the community;
- changes to local schools;
- changes to local youth clubs;
- policy changes.

As with the health measures, the community will be central to defining which social outcomes are to be measured.

Generating outcomes

One approach to generating outcome measures is for an experienced evaluator to probe what a community project team hope to get from their project. This can involve not only asking them to list outcomes that they hope to see, but also outcomes which they would associate with failure.

> 'For example, if the program is trying to tackle the problem of alcohol, people usually nominate success criteria such as reductions in alcohol intake, change of server policies and so on. Once these are listed and discussed the next thing to ask is 'What if (project name) makes no difference to these things? Could the project still be successful in some way? Are there any other types of things you would consider to be good outcomes of this project?' After some reflection, it is only then that one is likely to hear back such things like 'If the Council continues to involve us in service planning' or 'If the Steering Committee continues and takes up some new issues' or 'If groups get better at fighting for what they want'.'[119]

---

119. Hawe P 1994, pp 204–205.

○ ○

Evaluation at the Heeley Health Project

'For us the key area is to examine critically whether we are in fact meeting the overall aims and objectives of the project. The most recent Northern College report says "... the range of activities, the numbers involved and the focus on priority groups of local people are indicators that the project is achieving what it set out to do."'[120]

7.4 Qualitative research methods

Although it is not the function of this guide to describe particular research methods, the guide would not be complete without some discussion of the role of qualitative research methods in community development. This section draws on a series of seven articles from the *British Medical Journal* (Pope C and Mays N 1995; Mays N and Pope C 1995a; Mays N and Pope C 1995b; Britten N 1995; Kitzinger J 1995; Jones J and Hunter D 1995; Keen J and Packwood P 1995).

Quantitative research methods are well established in medicine and are particularly characterised by large-scale epidemiological studies. While these methods are essential in studying certain phenomena, they are of little value in studying non-quantifiable data. On the other hand, much that is non-quantifiable is of importance (e.g. culture, attitudes and subjective meanings are critically important in health, yet these cannot be quantified).[121] Qualitative research methods have been developed to study such phenomena.

The goal of qualitative research has been described as:

> ... the development of concepts which help us to understand social phenomena in natural (rather than experimental) settings, giving due emphasis to the meanings, experiences, and views of all the participants.[122]

This matches well with community development where: (a) the community is a natural rather than an experimental setting, and (b) workers tend to emphasise the importance of the views and values of the community.

120. Heller T 1994, p 13.
121. Popay J, Rogers A, Williams G 1995.
122. Pope C and Mays N 1995, p 43.

In community development, qualitative research tries to answer questions such as:

- what is happening to the community and its health?
- why?
- what changes do people want?
- how might they be provided?

Although none of these questions yields a quantitative answer, they can be used to explore experiences, views and wishes, which might lead to later quantitative research. This emphasises that qualitative and quantitative research are not in competition with one another. Each has its role and each can complement the other. For example, qualitative work can:

- be used as a precursor to quantitative work, helping to identify what parameters might be measured;
- supplement quantitative work by providing an alternative view
- be used where quantitative methods are not applicable.[123]

Quantitative research is often concerned with collecting data and deriving laws which can be used to make predictions. Qualitative research, on the other hand, is more concerned with understanding. 'The emphasis is not so much on prediction, as on being able to make actions intelligible ....'[124]

Rigour in qualitative research

The non-numeric basis of qualitative research attracts the criticism that it lacks rigour. Mays and Pope describe strategies which can ensure rigour in qualitative research, including:

- the use of systematic research design, data collection, interpretation and communication – just as in quantitative research;
- the creation of an account of the methods and data which can stand independently so that another researcher could carry out the same work and expect to come to the same conclusions;
- the production of a clear explanation of what has been studied.[125]

---

123. Pope C and Mays N 1995, p 44.
124. Murphy E and Mattson B 1992, p 87.
125. Mays N and Pope C, 1995, p 110.

They then provide a checklist for assessing qualitative research. This can be turned around to produce a checklist for planning qualitative research. This has been done in the box below.

Checklist for planning qualitative research

❏ Make your theoretical framework and methods used at each stage explicit.

❏ Describe the context clearly.

❏ Choose a sampling strategy that you can justify and describe.

❏ Ensure that your sampling strategy is theoretically comprehensive to ensure the generalisability of your analysis (e.g. have you covered the full range of individuals and settings?).

❏ Describe in detail how you did your fieldwork.

❏ Ensure that all your evidence (notes, records, etc.) could be inspected independently.

❏ Describe and justify your data analysis methods, ensuring that they relate to the original research questions.

❏ Get at least one other researcher to repeat your analysis to ensure reliability.

❏ Where appropriate, use quantitative methods to test qualitative conclusions.

❏ Seek out, and show that you have sought out, observations that might contradict your conclusions.

❏ Present your account systematically in a form that would satisfy a sceptical reader.[126]

Qualitative methods

The following qualitative methods might be considered for community development research. In each case, more detail can be found in the cited source.

---

126. Mays N and Pope C, 1995, p 112.

Observational methods

These methods involve the systematic observation of what people do and say, so overcoming the discrepancies between what people say they do and what they actually do.[127] For example, in the box below, the mother training sessions were tape-recorded as part of the evaluation.

Qualitative interviews

Qualitative interviews are used to explore things like behaviours and beliefs in an open-ended way. They tend to use a topic guide with an open agenda, rather than a list of closed questions. The openness requires special skills on the part of interviewers to ensure that they find out what it is they wish to know without destroying the interview format.[128] In the community mothers programme (see box below) qualitative interviews were used with the health visitors.

Analysing qualitative interviews can be difficult, especially if they have been tape-recorded.

○ ○

Evaluating a community mothers project

In this project experienced mothers were given training to work with less experience mothers, in partnership with health visitors. Three sets of qualitative evaluation data were obtained in order to enhance the reliability of the conclusions. The methods used were:

❏ ten families who had been visited regularly by community mothers were interviewed using a topic list. The interviews were recorded either by note-taking or tape-recording, according to the interviewer's skill

❏ six two-hour monthly community mother training sessions were tape-recorded

❏ four individual sessions between the researcher and community mothers were recorded

❏ the four health visitors involved completed an open-ended questionnaire.[129]

---

127. Mays N and Pope C 1995, p182.
128. Britten N 1995, p 251.
129. Suppiah C 1994.

Focus groups

Focus groups are a form of collective interviewing. Run by a facilitator, the participants talk among themselves with the facilitator listening but not participating. Such groups are thought to be capable of revealing far more than one-to-one interviews. Their power is widely recognised in marketing where they are a major method for exploring consumers' views on products and services. Kitzinger, in the health context, recommends their use to:

- highlight respondents' attitudes, priorities, language and frameworks of understanding;
- encourage communication from participants;
- identify group norms and cultural values;
- provide insight into group social processes;
- encourage open conversation about embarrassing subjects and to permit the expression of criticism.[130]

The Delphi method

The Delphi method is used to try to identify a consensus, usually among a group of experts, in a way in which participants are not influenced by dominant or persuasive individuals. The participants do not meet. Instead, they contribute and respond to written views and predictions of the other members of the group. In community development, the method probably has most potential in research policy and strategy.[131]

Nominal group technique

In this technique, a group produces ideas which are ranked first by individuals, and then by the group, to reach a consensus view. While the method needs tight administration, it requires no special skills on the part of participants and so is appropriate for community development. It can easily be applied to group decision making about health needs and priorities for action.[132]

Rapid appraisal

This method has already been discussed earlier in this guide (see page 47).

130. Kitzinger J 1995, p 302.
131. Jones J and Hunter D 1995, p 377.
132. Jones J and Hunter D 1995, pp 377–8.

The spoke method

A more sophisticated measure of participation is the spoke method which provides a visual representation of participation, enabling before-and-after pictures to be drawn.[133] It measures participation on five scales:

- needs assessment;
- leadership;
- organisation;
- resource mobilisation;
- management.

For each of these, a continuum is developed with five steps, as in Figure 14.

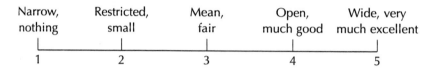

Figure 14 Ranking scale used for spoke method

The evaluation process is used to collect rankings for the five dimensions using this scale. Rankings might be separately collected for health staff, community leaders and participants. Each set of rankings creates a different visual image of the level of participation. Figure 15 shows the type of picture that results. In part 1 of the figure, the baseline rankings are shown. In part 2, a later set of rankings are given, and the shaded area shows the increase in participation. The inner pentagon joining all the rankings of 1 together indicates that this is the minimum possible ranking on each scale.

7.5 Planning an evaluation

If an evaluation of a community project is to succeed, it must not only be technically sound, but it must address issues that matter to the community, and the community must own the evaluation process. So, a particular concern in planning the evaluation is how to ensure full participation in the plan, its execution and its interpretation. Generally, this will mean the community controlling the evaluation, but having access to research expertise when they feel they need it.

---

133. Rifkin SB, Muller F and Bichmann W 1988.

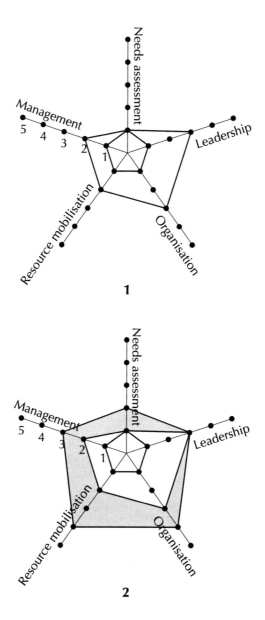

Figure 15 Before-and-after spoke representations of participation[134]

Table 12 suggests a possible nine-step process for planning, implementing and interpreting the evaluation.

134. Rifkin SB, Muller F and Bichmann W 1988, Figures 2 and 3 (adapted).

Table 12 Planning, implementing and interpreting an evaluation

Stage	Rationale
1 Clarify the aims and objectives of the project	A project needs to be very clear about what it is trying to achieve before it plans its evaluation. If this stage is overlooked, there is a risk that the evaluation will look at issues that are not important to the participants
2 Decide what process and output measures you think are important	A number of possible measures of both process and outcome have already been discussed in this section, but there are many other possible measures
3 Choose the methods that you will use to collect data	The methods will be largely qualitative. Some possible methods have been discussed above
4 Decide how the data will be recorded	One source of error in research is poor data recording. A well-designed data recording system will be clear to all those who have to use it, and simple to use
5 Agree who will collect the data and when	In a community development project, the community may well do the data collection. The project will need to agree who will undertake this
6 Train data collectors as needed	Most data collection requires specific skills. For example, interviewing is a specific skill, and training needs to be available for those who have no experience of it
7 Analyse the data	Once the data has been collected, it needs to be collated, processed and analysed so that the project can begin to interpret it
8 Interpret the data	This stage asks, 'What does the data mean?' The community is likely to be extensively involved at this stage
9 Share and publicise the findings	Finally, the outcomes of the evaluation need to be shared throughout the community

Appendix 1

Planning checklist

The following checklist can be adapted to help plan an initiative and monitor its development. It is written in the form of a number of issues that need to be considered by any group wishing to run a community development project.

Issue	Guide sections
1 Why does the group wish to use community development for health, and what benefits does it seek?	2.1, 2.3, 3.2, 3.3, 3.4, 3.5
2 What does the group mean by 'community'?	2.2
3 How will the initiative link with the practice's priorities and the priorities of the other participating organisations?	3.1
4 How will the group decide which agencies to approach?	4.1, 4.8
5 Which structure does the group prefer?	4.1
6 Who does the group see as the initiative's stakeholders?	4.2
7 Which methods does the group favour for needs assessment?	4.4
8 How does the group see the role of community workers and project working/management groups?	4.9, 4.10
10 What skills will your initiative need?	5.1, 5.2
11 How might training be provided?	5.3, 5.4, 5.5
12 How will the group decide the purposes of the evaluation of the initiative?	7.1
13 How will the group decide which process and outcome measures it will use?	7.2, 7.3
14 How will the group make a start?	4.3

Appendix 2

Addresses and contacts

Training resources

CETU. *Training and How Not to Panic*. CETU. Tel: 01422 357394. Guidelines for trainers working with community groups and voluntary organisations.

CETU. *Training and How to Enjoy It*. CETU. Tel: 01422 357394. Training exercises for community groups and voluntary organisations.

Community Development Training Group Wearside. *Learning the Ropes*. North East Regional Training Group, Sunderland. Tel: 0191 567 7051. A video and handbook for voluntary management committees.

Federation of Community Work Training Groups 1990. *Learning for Action: Community work and participative training*. London: Association of Metropolitan Authorities.

Federation of Community Work Training Groups. *Training Manual 1: Setting up a community work skills course*. Sheffield: Federation of Community Work Training Groups. Tel: 0114 273 9391.

Hampshire and South Coast CWTG. *A Training Manual for Stage 1 Course in Community Work*. Hampshire and South Coast CWTG. Tel: 01705 834809.

Haris V (ed) 1994. *Community Work Skills Manual*. Newcastle-upon-Tyne: Association of Community Workers. Tel: 0191 272 4341.

Henderson P 1989. *Promoting Active Learning*. Cambridge: National Extension College.

Sapin K and Watters G. *Learning from Each Other: Handbook for participative learning and community work learning programmes*. Greater Manchester Community Work Training Group. Tel: 0161 953 4117.

Standards and qualifications

Federation of Community Work Training Groups
356 Glossop Road
Sheffield S10 2HW
Tel: 0114 2739391

Central Council for Education and Training in Social Work
(CCETSW)
Derbyhire House
St Chad's Street
London WC1H 8AD
Tel: 0171 278 2455

City and Guilds
1 Giltspur Street
London EC1A 9DD
Tel: 0171 294 2468

SCOTVEC
Hanover House
24 Douglas Street
Glasgow G2 7NQ
Tel: 0141 248 7900

Organisations

Rural community councils with community/health care contacts

Sonia Minney
Rural Carers Support Worker
Avon Community Council
Church House
74 Long Ashton Road
Long Ashton
Bristol BS18 9LE
Tel: 01275 393837

Sarah Ward
Rural Community Care Worker
Community Council for Berkshire
Epping House
55 Russell Street
Reading RG1 7XG
Tel: 01734 566556/612000

Trisha Brady
Community Care Officer
Cleveland Council for Voluntary Service
47 Princes Road
Middlesborough
Cleveland TS1 4BG
Tel: 01642 240651/2

Pam Rabett (Carers' Co-ordinator)/Trevor Moses (Mental Health
Co-ordinator)
Cornwall Rural Community Council
9A River Street
Truro
Cornwall TR1 2SQ
Tel: 01872 73952

Graham Hunt
Community Care Development Officer
Derbyshire Rural Community Council
Church Street
Wirksworth
Derby DE4 4EY
Tel: 01629 824797

Jen Anderson
Rural Health and Community Care Project Officer
Hampshire Council of Community Service
Beaconsfield House
Andover Road
Winchester SO22 6AT
Tel: 01962 854971

Catherine Jackson-Read (Community Care Liaison, Worcs) and Anne
Bibbings (Community Care Liaison, Herefordshire)
Community Council of Hereford and Worcestershire
Great Malvern Station
Station Approach
Malvern
Worcestershire WR14 3AU
Tel: 01684 573334

Linda Small
Community Care Development Officer
Community Council for Hertfordshire
2 Townsend Avenue
St Albans AL1 3SG
Tel: 01727 852298

Susan Eley
Manager of Carebuilders Lincs
Community Council of Lincolnshire
Church Lane
Sleaford
Lincs NG34 7DF
Tel: 01529 302466

Pat Moloney (Deputy Director) or Liz Mandeville (Village Care
Organiser)
Nottinghamshire Rural Community Council
Minster Chambers
Church Street
Southwell NG25 0HD
Tel: 01636 815267

Jacky Martin
Carers Manager
Suffolk ACRE
Alexandra House
Rope Walk
Ipswich IP4 1LZ
Tel: 01473 264595

Pat Buesnel
East Sussex Officer
Surrey Voluntary Service Council
Astolat
Coniers Way
New Inn Lane
Burpham
Guildford
Surrey GU4 7HL
Tel: 01483 566072

Other organisations

Association of Community Workers
Stephenson Building
Elswick Road
Newcastle-upon-Tyne NE4 6SQ
Tel: 0191 272 4341

Community Development Foundation
60 Highbury Grove
London N5 2AG

Community Development Foundation
Suite 326-328
Baltic Chambers
50 Wellington Street
Glasgow G2 6HJ
Tel: 0141 248 1924

Community Health UK
6 Terrace Walk
Bath BA1 1LN
Tel: 01225 462680

Federation of Community Work Training Groups
356 Glossop Road
Sheffield S10 2HW
Tel 0114 2739391

National Council for Voluntary Organisations
Regent's Wharf
8 All Saints Street
London N1 9RL
Tel: 0171 713 6161

Scottish Council for Voluntary Organisations
19 Claremont Crescent
Edinburgh EH7 4QD

Standing Conference on Community Development
356 Glossop Road
Sheffield S10 2HW

Health Promotion Wales
(Helen Howson, Community Development Adviser)
Ffynnon-las
Ty Glas Avenue
Llanishen
Cardiff CF4 5DZ
Tel: 01222 752222

Bibliography

ACRE 1994. *Rural Life: Facts and figures*. Cirencester: ACRE.

Adams L 1989/ Healthy cities, healthy participation. *Health Education Journal*; 48(4):179–182.

Agass M et al 1991. Patient participation in general practice: who participates? *British Journal of General Practice*; May:198–201.

Armstrong J and Henderson P (eds) 1992. *Putting the Community into Community Care: Report of a conference*. London: Community Development Foundation.

Arnstein SR 1969. A ladder of citizen participation. *AIP Journal*; July:216–224.

Ashton J and Luker K 1991. Quoted in Colin-Thomé 1994.

Association of Metropolitan Authorities 1993. *Local Authorities and Community Development: A strategic opportunity for the 1990s*. London: Association of Metropolitan Authorities.

Baker D and Burgess R 1993. *The Liaison between Voluntary Organisation and General Practice*. Dr Deborah Baker and Associates.

Barker J 1979. *Community Partnership: A community's perspective*. The Volunteer Centre.

Barton Watcombe and Hele (Torquay) Health Gain Initiative (nd). Notes supplied by Hilary Neve.

Beattie A 1991. Knowledge and control in health promotion: a test case for social policy and social theory. In Gabe J, Clanan M and Bury M 1991.

Bjärås G 1991. Can a community development model be used for health programmes in an industrialised country? *International Journal of Health Planning and Management*; 6:209–219.

Brittan Y 1994. *Working through Localities in Berkshire, Buckinghamshire, Northamptonshire and Oxfordshire to Shape Commissioning for the Future*. Oxford: Anglia and Oxford Regional Health Authority.

Britten N 1995. Qualitative interviews in medical research. *British Medical Journal*; 311:251–253.

Broady M and Hedley R 1989. *Working Partnerships: Community development in local authorities*. London: Bedford Square Press.

Brown I 1994. Community and participation for general practice: perceptions of general practitioners and community nurses. *Social Science Medicine*; 39(3):335–344.

Browne D 1994. Brockenhurst Healthy Village Project. *Southampton Medical Journal*.

Browne D. Healthy Villages in *Occasional Paper 71 Rural General Practice*. Royal College of General Practitioners.

Bryar R and Fisk L 1994. Setting up a community health house. *Health Visitor*; 67(6):203-205.

CBH Newsletter (nd).

Chamberlain A 1992. Taking community development out of the project mould – one health authority's experience. *Community Health Action*; 25:17–19.

Chaplin J 1992. Feeling good in Heeley. *Community Action Health*; 23:9–11.

Cohen Z *et al.* 1994. *Salford Locality Health Needs Assessment Project: Final research report*. Salford and Trafford Health Commission.

Colin-Thomé D 1994. A fundholder's support for community participation. In Heritage Z (ed) 1994, pp 14–16.

Consumer Involvement Project 1993. *Locality Project: Overview, methodology and conclusions*. The Health Commission for Wiltshire and Bath.

Consumer Involvement Project 1994. *What's in a Word?* The Health Commission for Wiltshire and Bath.

Consumer Involvement Project (nd). *Involving Consumers in Health Care: The Voluntary Sector Contribution*. The Health Commission for Wiltshire and Bath.

Department of Health 1995. *Variations in Health: What can the Department of Health and the NHS do?* Department of Health.

Dowswell T, Drinkwater C and Morley V 1994. Developing an inner city health resource centre. In Heritage Z (ed) 1994.

Drennan V (ed)1988. *Health Visitors and Groups: Politics and practice*. Oxford: Heinemann Nursing.

Drennan V 1986. *Effective Health Education in the Inner City: Report of a feasibility study examining community development approaches*. London: Health Education Department, Paddington and North Kensington Health Authority.

Drennan V (nd). *Working in a Different Way: A research project examining community work methods and health visiting*. London: Paddington and North Kensington Health Authority.

Ewles L and Simnett I 1992. *Promoting Health: A practical guide*. Harrow: Scutari Press.

Ewles, L, Miles U and Velleman G 1995. Promoting heart health through community empowerment. *Community Health Action*; 35:12–14.

Farrant W 1986. 'Health for All' in the Inner City. District Health Promotion Group, Paddington and North Kensington Health Authority.

Farrant W and Russell J 1985. *HEC Publications: A case study in the production, distribution and use of health information. Final report of the Health Education Publications Project*. Institute of Education, University of London.

Federation of Community Work Training Groups 1990. *Learning for Action: Community work and participative training*. London: Association of Metropolitan Authorities.

Federation of Community Work Training Groups 1992. *Training Manual 1: Setting up a community work skills course*. Sheffield: Federation of Community Work Training Groups.

Fennell J 1992. *Health Care in Rural England*. Cirencester: ACRE.

Funnell R, Oldfield K, Speller V 1995. *Towards Healthier Alliances: A tool for planning, evaluating and developing healthy alliances*. Health Education Authority.

Gabe J, Calnan M and Bury M 1991. *The Sociology of the Health Service*. London: Routledge.

Harris V 1994. *Community Work Skills Manual*. Association of Community Workers.

Hawe P 1994. Capturing the meaning of 'community' intervention evaluation: some contributions from community psychology. *Health Promotion International*; 9(3):199–210.

Health Promotion Wales 1995. *Getting Started: Proceedings of December 1 Seminar*. Cardiff: Health Promotion Wales.

Health Promotion Wales 1996. *Monitoring and Evaluation Scheme: Action booklet*. Cardiff: Health Promotion Wales.

The Healthcare Forum (nd). *What Creates Health: Individual and communities respond*. San Francisco: The Healthcare Forum.

Healthy Sheffield Support Team 1993. *Community Development and Health: The way forward in Sheffield*. Sheffield: Healthy Sheffield Support Team.

Heller T 1994. The Heeley Health Project. In Heritage Z (ed) 1994.

Henderson P 1989. *Promoting Active Learning*. Cambridge: National Extension College.

Heritage Z (ed) 1994. *Community Participation in Primary Care*. The Royal College of General Practitioners.

Hunt S 1990. Building alliances: professional and political issues in community participation. Examples from a health and community development project. *Health Promotion International*; 5(3):179–185.

Jones J and Hunter D 1995. Consensus methods for medical and health services research. *British Medical Journal*; 311:376–380.

Joule N 1992. *User Involvement in Medical Audit: A spoke in the wheel or a link in the chain?* London: The Greater London Association of Community Health Councils.

Keen J and Packwood T 1995. *British Medical Journal*; 311:444–446.

King's Fund 1994. *Community-Oriented Primary Care. A resource for developers*. London: King's Fund.

King's Fund Centre 1986. *Papers from a Conference 'Community Development in Health: Addressing the Confusions'*. London: King's Fund Centre.

Kitzinger J 1995. Introducing focus groups. *British Medical Journal*; 311:299–302.

Knowles M 1975. *Self-directed Learning: A Guide for learners and teachers*. New York: Association Press.

Knowles M 1990. *The Adult Learner: A neglected species* 4th ed. Houston: Gulf Publishing Company.

Labyrinth Training and Consultancy (nd). *Helping You to Assess Health Needs.* (Brochure)

Labyrinth Training nd. *Moving On: A report of the National Community Health Conference.*

Lassiter PG 1992. A community development perspective for rural nursing. *Family and Community Health*; 14(4):29–39.

Laughlin S and Black D (eds) 1995. *Poverty and Health: Tools for Change: Ideas analysis information action.* Birmingham: The Public Health Alliance.

Laurie E 1994. Ideas for the evaluation of community participation initiatives. In Heritage Z (ed) 1994, pp33–35.

Leyden R, Martins M and Russell J 1994. The politics of health information. *Critical Public Health*; 5(1):32–43.

Livingstone A and Widgery D 1990. The new new general practice: the changing philosophies of primary care. *British Medical Journal*; 301 3 October.

Maxwell R and Weaver N (eds) 1984. *Public Participation in Health: Towards a Clearer View.* London: King Edward's Hospital Fund for London.

Mays N and Pope C 1995a. Observational methods in health care settings. *British Medical Journal*; 311:182–184.

Mays N and Pope C 1995b. Rigour and qualitative research. *British Medical Journal*; 311: 109–112.

McDiarmid P and Gosling A 1992. Wells Park Health Project: joy, caring and better health. *Community Health Action*; 23:12–13.

Murphy E and Mattson B 1992. Qualitative research and family practice: a marriage made in heaven? *Family Practice*; 9(1):85–91.

Murray S A (nd). *Chogoria, Kenya: Case Study of a Community Development.*

Murray S A (nd). MD *Thesis: abstract.*

Murray SA 1996. *Letter in British Medical Journal*; 312:250.

Murray SA, Tapson J, Turnbull L, McCallum J, Little A 1994. 'Listening to local voices: adapting rapid appraisal to assess health and social needs in general practice' *British Medical Journal*; 1994(308):698–700.

Neve H (nd). *Community Assessment in General Practice: Dissertation summary.*

NHS Centre for Reviews and Dissemination 1995. *Review of the Research on the Effectiveness of Health Service Interventions to Reduce Variations in Health.* University of York.

Ong BN and Humphris G 1994. Prioritising needs with communities: rapid appraisal methods in health. In Popay J and Williams G (eds) 1994.

Papadakis E and Taylor-Gooby P 1987. Consumer attitudes and participation in state welfare. *Political Studies*; 35:467–481.

Pollitt C. Consuming passions. *The Health Service Journal.*

Pollock AM 1992. Local voices: The bankruptcy of the democratic process. *British Medical Journal*; 305 5 September:535–536.

Pollock AM 1995. Where should health services go: local authorities versus the NHS? *British Medical Journal*; 310 17 June:1580–1589.

Popay J and Williams G (eds) 1994. *Researching the People's Health.* London: Routledge.

Popay J, Rogers A, Williams G 1995. 'Qualitative research and the gingerbread man' *Health Education Journal*; 54(4):389–392.

Popay J, Williams G 1996. 'Public health research and lay knowledge' *Social Science Medicine*; 42(5):759–768.

Pope C and Mays N 1995. Reaching the parts other methods cannot reach: an introduction to qualitative methods in health and health services research. *British Medical Journal*; 311:42–45.

Prout A and Deverell K 1995. *Working with Diversity: Evaluating the MESMAC Project.* London: Health Education Authority.

Public Health Alliance 1992. *Community Development and Health: Reclaiming the national agenda.* Birmingham: The Public Health Alliance.

Research Unit in Health and Behavioural Change 1989. *Changing the Public Health.* Chichester: John Wiley and Sons Ltd.

Richardson A and Bray C 1987. *Promoting Health through Participation*. London: Policy Studies Institute.

Rifkin SB, Muller F and Bichmann W 1988. Primary health care: on measuring participation. *Social Science Medicine*; 26(9):931–940.

Roberts E 1990. *We Live There, We Should Know* ... Hartcliffe Health Project.

Russell J 1995. *A Review of Health Promotion in Primary Care*. The Greater London Association of Community Health Councils.

Rutherford G and Campbell D 1993. Helping people help themselves. *The Canadian Nurse*; 89(10):25–28.

Saunders L (ed) 1988. *Action for Health: Initiatives in local communities*. London: Community Projects Foundation.

Sim J, Moffat S and Menzies F 1994. Developing health information in Lothian: the influence of Wendy's work. *Critical Public Health*; 5(1):44–48.

Sinclair TA 1994. *Report of the African-Caribbean Community Development Health Worker*. Wells Park Health Project.

Sinclair TA 1994. *Summary of the African-Caribbean Community Development Health Worker Report*. Wells Park Health Project.

Smithies J nd. *The Community Health Movement: A personal view of current key issues and debates*.

Somerville G et al. 1984. *Community Development in Health: Addressing the confusions*. London: King's Fund Centre/London Community Health Resource/ Community Health Initiatives Resource Unit.

Southampton and South West Hampshire Health Authority 1996 *The Healthy Village*. Southampton and South West Hampshire Health Authority.

Suppiah C 1994. Working in partnership with community mothers. *Health Visitor*; 67(2):51–53. *Community Action Health*; 23:7–8.

Sykes W et al. 1992. *Listening to Local Voices: A guide to research methods*. Leeds: Nuffield Institute for Health Services Studies.

Taylor M 1992. *Signposts to Community Development*. London: Community Development Foundation.

Taylor P 1995. *Public Consumer Involvement: Developing a strategy.* Consumer Involvement Project

Taylor P and Upward J 1995. *Bridge Building for Effective User Involvement in Primary Care.* Birmingham Family Health Services Authority.

Thomas DN 1995. *Helping Communities to Better Health: The community development approach.* Cardiff: Health Promotion Wales.

Thornley P 1992. *Liverpool Healthy City: Investing in community empowerment.*

Thurnhurst C. *Poverty and Health in the City of Sheffield.* 1985

University of Salford 1994. *Resource Management in Primary Care: Final report of a development project.*

Watt A and Rodmell S 1988. Community involvement in health promotion: progress or panacea? *Health Promotion;* 2(4):359–368.

Webster G and Smithies J 1994. *Limeside Local Voices: A community-based survey of local health needs.* Labyrinth Training and Consultancy.

Wells Park Health Project 1994. *Report on Self-Assessment of Health and Health Care Needs by Young People in the Borough of Lewisham, South East London.* Wells Park Health Project.

Wells Park Health Project 1996. *Annual Report 1996.* Wells Park Health Project.

Williams SJ and Calnan M 1991. Key determinants of consumer satisfaction with general practice. *Family Practice;* 8(3):237–242.

Willmott P 1989. *Community Initiatives: Patterns and prospects.* London: Policy Studies Institute.

Wiltshire Voluntary Development Forum (nd). *Code of Good Practice on Consultation.* Wiltshire Voluntary Development Forum.

Winters M 1991. A national structure for community development of health. *Community Health Action;* 19 Spring:4.

World Health Organization 1981. Global *Strategy for Health for All by the Year 2000.* Geneva: WHO.

World Health Organization 1991. *Community Involvement in Health Development: Challenging health services.*